*Create your own dreams at the...*

# *Dreamweaver Bridal Studio*

**Custom Designed Wedding Gowns for that once-in-a-lifetime occasion**

*By Appointment Only*

*Shelly Barker, Owner and Designer*

***Reluctant Grooms***
1. Lazarus Rising
Anne Stuart
2. A Million Reasons Why
Ruth Jean Dale
3. Designs on Love
Gina Wilkins
4. The Nesting Instinct
Elizabeth August
5. Best Man for the Job
Dixie Browning
6. Not *His* Wedding!
Suzanne Simms

***Western Weddings***
7. The Bridal Price
Barbara Boswell
8. McCade's Woman
Rita Rainville
9. Cactus Rose
Stella Bagwell
10. The Cowboy and the Chauffeur
Elizabeth August
11. Marriage-Go-Round
Katherine Ransom
12. September Morning
Diana Palmer

***Instant Families***
13. Circumstantial Evidence
Annette Broadrick
14. Bundle of Joy
Barbara Bretton
15. McConnell's Bride
Naomi Horton
16. A Practical Marriage
Dallas Schulze
17. Love Counts
Karen Percy
18. Angel and the Saint
Emilie Richards

***Marriage, Inc.***
19. Father of the Bride
Cathy Gillen Thacker
20. Wedding of the Year
Elda Minger
21. Wedding Eve
Betsy Johnson
22. Taking a Chance on Love
Gina Wilkins
23. This Day Forward
Elizabeth Morris
24. The Perfect Wedding
Arlene James

***Make-Believe Matrimony***
25. The Marriage Project
Lynn Patrick
26. It Happened One Night
Marie Ferrarella
27. Married?!
Annette Broadrick
28. In the Line of Duty
Doreen Roberts
29. Outback Nights
Emilie Richards
30. Love for Hire
Jasmine Cresswell

***Wanted: Spouse***
31. Annie in the Morning
Curtiss Ann Matlock
32. Mail-Order Mate
Louella Nelson
33. A Business Arrangement
Kate Denton
34. Mail Order Man
Roseanne Williams
35. Silent Sam's Salvation
Myrna Temte
36. Marry Sunshine
Anne McAllister

***Runaway Brides***
37. Runaway Bride
Karen Leabo
38. Easy Lovin'
Candace Schuler
39. Madeline's Song
Stella Bagwell
40. Temporary Temptress
Christine Rimmer
41. Almost a Bride
Raye Morgan
42. Strangers No More
Naomi Horton

***Solution: Wedding***
43. To Choose a Wife
Phyllis Halldorson
44. A Most Convenient Marriage
Suzanne Carey
45. First Comes Marriage
Debbie Macomber
46. Make-believe Marriage
Carole Buck
47. Once Upon a Time
Lucy Gordon
48. Taking Savanah
Pepper Adams

Marriage, Inc.

# BETSY JOHNSON

# WEDDING EVE

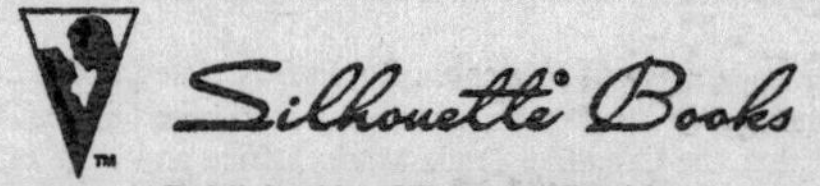


Published by Silhouette Books
America's Publisher of Contemporary Romance

ISBN 0-373-30121-9

WEDDING EVE



Celebrity Wedding Certificates published by permission of Donald Ray Pounders from *Celebrity Wedding Ceremonies*.



This edition published by arrangement with Harlequin Books S.A.



**Printed in U.S.A.**

## A Letter from the Author

Dear Reader,

I came to appreciate the fine art of weddings when my oldest son decided it was his turn. His wife-to-be lived in Texas and he, being in the military, was with her. Both of them, however, wanted the event to happen here, in our home state of Utah. That meant—outside of a frustratingly few long-distance directions—I was in charge.

Making decisions has never been easy for me. Now, here I was, faced with the task of organizing a major life event for a young woman I'd never met. It's difficult to explain the kind of dread I felt knowing that every wrong choice I made would likely be rehashed in my son's marriage bed for the duration of his natural life.

Well, events proceeded. The countdown began when the dress arrived in a carefully packed box. Because of scheduling conflicts, the kids flew in only three days before the ceremony. They should have come sooner.

My daughter-in-law-to-be had ordered several alterations to the dress, then sent it here without having time to try it on. Two days before the wedding we discovered that instead of an adjusted hemline, her once-perfect size nine had been altered to a narrow size seven. The absolute panic of knowing that the satin-encased zipper could not go any higher was the conception of Shelly's story.

We did manage to find a woman with a sense of humor and a magic needle. And, yes, the wedding was everything my son and his young bride hoped for. Would I go through it again? Not without a doctor's release. Enjoy!

Betsy Johnson

## *Chapter One*

The connection was poor, lousy, bad; breaking, wavering, jamming with interference. Garbling words about machines, bridal bowers and hell.

"What?" Switching the receiver from her right ear to her left, Shelly Barker deposited the sack of groceries on the counter and shrugged out of her heavy winter coat. She'd walked in, had just had enough time to shut the door, when the phone rang. "What did you say?" She raised her voice over the paper crackle of static. "I can't understand you."

"We have—" the caller's voice faded out for a few moments, then came back through a long, tin tunnel "—up here. Four days. That's all we have left. She—"

For an instant, as her mind arranged bits and pieces of the fragmented sentences into a somewhat coherent pattern, and with the line discharges popping like gum in her ear, Shelly stared at the cobweb-dust string floating from the light fixture over the table. If she ever got to it, that string, and many like it, was next on her chore list. "Will you speak up a bit more, please. I still can't hear much of what you're saying."

"I couldn't stop her." The caller's voice splintered, "didn't realize . . . too late." The words disintegrated before they reached their target. " . . . Bring your machine."

Shelly's heart took a quick, lurching dip. That's what she'd thought she heard the first time. The meaning behind that specific request could range from disaster to tragedy. At this late date, a call from a client's family was enough to blank all rational thought from Shelly's mind. All thought except for one.

She looked to the kitchen window and found that the heavy, dull clouds hindering this very conversation were even now pushing a blanket of gray down to cover the foothills. Normally, Shelly didn't consider herself timid, but she did have a slight inhibition when it came to driving in Utah's high-winter storms. In less than an hour, the sun would set, the temperature would drop to well below zero and the roads through the mountain passes would turn to slicks of ice.

"Mrs. Sutherland—" Shelly kept her eyes on the window and yelled to be heard "—I'll drive up tomorrow." *After the trucks had been up to plow, after the roads were clear and sanded.* "First thing. I'll—"

"No!" The voice was quick and thin, "can't wait. Only four days." The line spat, "Governor accepted." The air snapped with interference and urgency. "Family on their way up . . . please, tonight."

In the end it was the word *please* that settled the matter.

Basically, Shelly Barker had two philosophies in life, the first being, What Goes Around Comes Around. One could not refuse a "pretty please" from a society matron as influential as Megan Sutherland and expect a glowing reference afterward. The Sutherlands were an old, powerful family in the Intermountain area, charismatic enough to be featured in the local society pages with nearly monthly regularity. And since Shelly's second philosophy was that it was more pleasant to live long and prosper than not to, and since her main source of advertising came by word-of-mouth referrals from families like the Sutherlands, it was a case of shelving her own small phobias and going quickly.

She rushed around the house like a mad thing, storing groceries, loading necessary supplies into the car, changing clothes. Minutes of waning daylight ticked by in an involved telephone conversation with her brother. Despite her rush, it was still after six when she stopped to gas her Bronco, then maneuvered its wheels onto the snow-packed interstate heading east and began the drive up Parleys Canyon.

Snow battered the windshield. Instantly the heavy white stuff was transformed by the heater-warmed glass into sheets of slushy ice that weighed, and thwarted, the furious swish of the wipers. The illuminated clock on the dash told Shelly that she had been on the road for nearly an hour, but through the howling wind, there was no way of knowing how many miles the time represented. She'd forgot to set her trip meter, lost radio reception right after the third travel advisory warning, and she could not see any anchoring landmark beyond the red of the taillights in front.

When she first saw the glow she blinked. Instinct told her she hadn't come far enough for the lights to be those that marked the turnoff interchange into Park City, although hope wanted them to be.

As she crept ever forward, the specter took on distinguishable shapes and substance; orange emergency flares, blue-and-red lights of the canyon patrol. Downshifting, she held her breath in case the shaky release of it forced her, too, off the upcoming curve in the highway.

She took the curve at a crawl, edging past the barrier flares, the flash and confusion, the sirens. By the look of it, every emergency vehicle in the canyon was on hand to untangle the mass of overturned semitrucks and jackknifed trailers. Human shapes surged through the blowing wind. Half a dozen passenger cars, slewed back to front, fender to bumper, were tipped and helpless, trapped in the highway median.

The officer came out of the storm, flagging the car ahead to a stop. Shelly inched up behind, shifted into neutral and waited. The scene was caught in her headlights, and she watched the officer speak to the first driver. He talked for quite a few moments, gesturing now and then toward several people huddled together by a patrol vehicle off to one side. They must, she guessed, be the orphans of this storm who belonged to the cars in the median. She wondered how long they had been stranded in the frigid cold.

When the officer raised his hand again, a woman tugged two children out of the patrol car and rushed them through the wind. A man detached himself from the outside group and joined the woman. Once they were settled in the conscripted car, it pulled out beyond the barrier.

Rolling her own window down, Shelly waited for the officer's approach. "Evening, ma'am," he said, and touched the brim of his hat.

"Officer," she said, returning his greeting. She hoped she had enough room for the remaining casualties. With no headlights at all behind her, hers had probably been the last car in before they had closed the canyon.

"Not planning to drive on through to Rock Springs tonight, I hope?"

"No," she said, and sympathized with his tired grin. Already the cold and snow blowing in from the open window was making her shiver, and the officer wouldn't get to go home until the accident was cleared away. "I'm turning off at the Park City exit."

"In that case—" the officer lifted his hand "—I've got one more passenger needing a ride. You'll be safe, miss, I guarantee it. Great guy, been out in this from the first. Wouldn't go, though, until everyone else was taken care of."

Before Shelly could agree or object or tell the officer she'd rather rescue cranky children than a hero, the dome light came on when the passenger door opened. A flight bag and an attaché were tossed into the back. In the next instant, the right front bucket seat was invaded by a hoarfrosted, windblown man who, when he turned toward her, caused her vocal cords to malfunction.

But not her brain. He seemed familiar, vaguely. The shape and form, his shadow and substance; his size nebulously overwhelming. While it occurred to Shelly to close her mouth, for a moment, she couldn't take her eyes away. For one split second in time, she felt intimidated. With the unconscious instinct of all females sensing a dominant male threat, she lifted her head in alert. Then, in a blink of an eye—faster even—the sensation was gone.

With other problems to solve, the officer tapped on the window to get her moving, and Shelly waved to let him know that the situation was under control. Shifting into first gear, she nosed the Bronco cautiously back onto Interstate 80.

Her passenger was cold, chilled to the bone. Moving stiffly, he redirected the heater's side vent and spread his fingers toward the stream of air. Quickly, Shelly adjusted the heater to power blast. "Are you all right? Does this help?"

The man grunted, fumbling with his seat belt, "Thanks." He blinked, shaking his head. "I should have known better than to try this drive without boots and a heavier coat. I appreciate the ride, Ms....?"

"Shelly." Her grin was quick and sharp. She did have the prerequisite portfolio, but lacked the accessorized, navy blue business suit necessary to transform an average miss or missus woman into a Ms. "Just Shelly Barker."

"I'm Dan." He didn't smile, was too raw and stiff to think of it. Adjusting his useless topcoat around his legs, he slumped back against the seat and let the heater begin the thawing process.

"What happened?" she asked after a moment.

For more warmth, he shoved his hand deep into his coat pocket. "The whole mess could have been avoided." When he sighed, the sound was tinged with disgust. "Me, and the rest of the cars you saw piled in the median, were following the convoy line of truckers going up. Wind knocked the first semi across all three lanes and into the gully wash on the right...the next semi slowed, but fishtailed...then the next. We saw it coming, those of us paying attention. Unfortunately, the driver directly in back of the convoy was not. Of course—" he slouched further into the seat and snorted "—the driver of the damned car was a woman."

One by one the downy fine hairs on the nape of Shelly's neck rose and bristled. Her nose wrinkled, and her mouth pursed, turning down. She didn't appreciate men with superior attitudes. Who, she wondered, was this guy? And why had fate chosen *her* to foist him on?

The deep breath she took was calmly measured, and the voice she used was deliberately bland. "I can pull over and let you out. Perhaps you'd like to wait for a male driver to come along."

Dan opened his mouth, then closed it. He sensed the tiniest bit of militancy in his benefactress. All right, he conceded, the comment he'd made was snotty, but a woman *had* been in the car ahead, she *hadn't* been paying attention and because of her, four additional vehicles had needlessly gone off the road, his sideways and rear first.

"Look," he said, pinching the bridge of his nose hard, "I didn't mean that the way it sounded, exactly. I'm tired and cold, and a man might just as well have been driving as a woman. I'm sorry."

Shelly felt her outraged little nape bristles begin to stand down and relax. She wasn't much on grudge holding, and a note in his voice had sounded sincere. It frustrated her that in the dim glare of the dash, she could not see distinctly, not precise details. His face was shadowed angles and hard planes. His dark eyes, glittered as they studied her across the separating distance. He was all male bulk and presence, occupying space she was used to having empty. His scent replaced what was familiar and comfortable to her, filling the car with the musk of damp wool, the crisp sharpness of cold, clean skin, the faint spice of after-shave.

He did, she guessed, deserve the benefit of the doubt, barely. "Okay."

"Are you going all the way into town?"

"Into, through and a bit beyond." She inhaled a lungful of long-forgotten man smells and returned some of her attention to the road ahead. "You're welcome to ride along as far as you like."

"Thanks," he said again. "I'll take you up on the offer." After a thoughtful moment he asked, "Why are you out in this? On your way home?"

"No, I live in the valley."

"Up to do some night skiing?"

"Not hardly," she drawled, and swallowed a spurt of laughter. He couldn't have been more wrong. Not only could she not afford to live in the exclusive resort town, but in the normal course of events, nothing short of a catastrophe could pry her out into a subzero, high-mountain snowstorm.

Her mouth pulled in a wry, lopsided smile when she looked at her passenger. Of course, since it was her destiny to be a superwoman tonight anyway, she would get the chatty version of male damsel in distress.

A sudden wind gust slammed down through the canyon, heaving from the left side, shoving on the right. The steering wheel pulled under her inattention, and Shelly immediately tightened her grip, forcing her total concentration back on the road. Shuddering under the pressure, the Bronco balked.

For a moment she thought the wheel would be torn from her hands. Perhaps she was overreacting, but the guardrail loomed too close in her headlights. An icy kind of fear squeezed her heart as she eased up on the gas. Anxiety coiled. The muscles in her foot trembled from the strain of keeping just the right, light pressure on the pedal.

"For hell's sake, woman, it is legal to go faster than five miles an hour on this highway. Even in this weather!"

His voice grated, banging her nerves in the silence. Shelly snapped around. Okay, so she *was* crawling, and he was probably hungry besides being wet and cold. He was tired. She was cranky. But whatever, she vowed, she'd done to deserve this man tonight, she would never, ever, do again.

"I," she enunciated carefully, "am not the one who left the car back in the median."

The wind raged and shuddered again. She turned her head to ease the sudden tension in her neck, taking slow breaths, and consciously fighting the panic.

"Hey." Dan saw a glimpse of something through the shadows. "Are you okay?"

It took a moment for her to answer. "I get a little... nervous through here," she said at last.

Fatigue pulled at Dan's mouth, and a momentary confusion narrowed his brown eyes. "A little nervous" didn't describe the high strain in her voice. He took the time for a longer look at the woman next to him.

Her attention was fixed on the ice rink of a road, and she gripped the steering wheel with pale, rigid hands. Shadows played over her profile, stripping out the color of her hair and eyes to a nondescript gray. Her body was bundled in layers of heavy winter fabric—jeans, shirt, jacket—revealing no feminine mysteries, giving no clue.

Yet, because he was an observant man, Dan knew at least three things about her. She was not prone to idle chitchat. In her voice he'd heard the definite lushness of laughter as well as anger. And she was tough. He recognized determination and saw by the set jut of her jaw that she was used to fighting her own battles. Impulsively, for a split second, he felt his hand reaching out to reassure. He was not, however, an impulsive man and drew back.

"Would talking help?" he offered instead.

"No... yes. The thing is, I don't do well in storms after dark. I can't seem to help it." Shelly shook her head and dared to flex the cramped fingers of one hand. "My mother was killed in this very canyon." Of course, Claire Barker had been in a tearing hurry to get away from her family, with her suitcases stacked in the trunk and her purse full of getaway cash taken from the savings account. Rationally, Shelly knew her mother's death involved more than just time of day and weather conditions, and yet...

She also knew she was rambling, talking much too fast, but it was as if his question had released a pressure valve, and she couldn't seem to shut it off.

"I try to keep her...my mother's...recklessness in mind and, really, I was too young when it happened to be paranoid now. But when I'm out, the memory nags. I get tense and..." Fighting for control, Shelly shut her mouth.

In the distance she could finally see the vague yellow haze of the interchange lights, but she and her passenger weren't home free yet, and she was wound tighter than a spring. She hated the knots in her stomach and the clammy, twisting feel of helpless fear.

"Everyone," Dan said quietly, filling the abrupt silence, "is afraid of something."

Her smile was a shade uncomfortable and blatantly disbelieving. "Oh? What are your nightmares?"

He shifted to a more comfortable position in the bucket seat and turned his head away to stare beyond his own image reflected in the window. He was under no obligation to tell this woman anything, and it didn't take owning a detective's badge to know she wasn't expecting much in the way of an answer. He had the distinct impression that she was not going to hold her breath for a great revelation.

Dan smiled to himself in the glass, a quick self-depreciating flash. Because he didn't have her attention, he was just perverse enough to want it. And because there was no pressure to do so, he was willing to share a side of himself he rarely, if ever, gave away. Light lent the darkness a shielding intimacy and self-revelation was easier under the hypnotic metronome swish of the wipers.

"My family," he murmured thoughtfully. "I have a fear of failing them." He closed his eyes. "The obligations...owing...keeping enough pieces back for me." Then, inexplicably, he grunted and mumbled a mild expletive and rolled his eyes. "My mother," he added, and his deep chuckle hinted of so many things, but of indulgence, too.

The echo of his laughter eased tense muscles and soothed ragged nerves. His confession unarmed Shelly as nothing else could have done. For one moment, the door she kept barred opened up, and for the first time in two years, a man looked through. She turned her head to smile directly into his eyes. "I have a brother," she said quietly, "whom I feel exactly the same way about."

And even with her hands still paralyzed around the wheel, she continued to smile.

By the time Shelly was through the interchange, she had decided to stop under the beacon-bright arches of the fast-food restaurant on the other side. The squint lines she'd developed peering blindly through the windshield were tautly drawn, and the tension in her neck and shoulders had her hunchbacked behind the wheel.

"Coffee?" she croaked hoarsely. "I'll buy."

She nearly fell on her rear getting out of the car. Her muscles had been frozen so long, they didn't follow the directions of her mind. There was no feeling in her legs and feet. She grabbed for the door.

"Hold on!" Dan got around as fast as he could. Not fast enough to save her—she'd done that for herself—but quick enough to offer an assisting hand should one be necessary.

Snow fell on her uncovered hair while the biting wind whipped strands of it across her face. Even through the heavy layers of clothing, Dan could feel the deep tremors that shook the small woman. Her fingers were locked onto the door handle, and as he subtly urged her to let go, he realized it wasn't a case of her not *wanting* to, but that she could not. He realized she had been much more than anxious. She had been battling the effects of a petrifying fear all the way up Parleys Canyon. This time, when the impulse came to him, he carried it through. Gently prying her fingers from the door, he held them. "You are..." In the eerie haze of the parking-lot lights and howling storm, his voice was haunting; a fluid, controlled blend of whisky warmth and tenor smoothness. ".... a brave woman." His face tipped down close to hers as he brushed his cold lips across the back of her hand in tribute.

"I am," she whispered back, shaken, unthinkingly brushing at the crystalline flakes on his shoulder, "a scaredy-cat crybaby. Anyway, this is a weird conversation to be having with a strange man."

"I may be unknown to you, but I am not strange. Would you be my friend, Shelly Barker?"

"I don't know." She ought to have stepped away, but instead she stayed to enjoy his whimsy and accept the supporting arm he offered. Snow hit her cheeks and chin and melted off her eyelashes. She wasn't unaware of his intentions, and she appreciated his tact. With a few well-chosen words, he'd helped her through panicked lunacy to laughter. "Don't you have a wife or dog for that?"

"I can't fit either in my condo." He let a trace of little-boy petulance entertain them as they walked to the restaurant's sidewalk.

"Well, in that case, I might consider it . . . if you buy the coffee."

"That," he said with a sniff, "is blackmail."

They pushed through the double glass doors and the warmth and noise assaulted their frozen senses. Shelly turned to deliver a teasing reply. "That is . . ."

Recognition was swift and stunning. Fate, Shelly decided, was definitely female; sniggering like crazy behind a dainty fickle hand. Of course, she'd drawn this particular prize in tonight's lottery. Hadn't she already been on her way to his front door?

For a few minutes, she had been liking Dan of the one name. There was, however, no question of a friendship between Shelly Barker and this man. Of all the people in the world to find on this dark and stormy night, she'd got a genuine Prince Charming, Daniel James Sutherland. A nearly tangible sense of loss wiped the smile from the blue of her eyes and pulled the full line of her mouth straight.

With a detached sort of interest, she studied what the shadows outside had only hinted at. He wasn't exceptionally tall, an inch either way shy of six feet, but he appeared so to her. She was used to looking up. Anyone over five-foot-two was taller than she was. With her back to the glass doors and not much room to step around, she admired his chest. As chest's went, Dan Sutherland's appeared to be better than average, deep and lean and covered by a fine lawn dress shirt that hadn't dared wrinkle. His shoulders were wide under, first, a silk-blend suit coat, then a damp, classically cut topcoat.

Looking all the way up to his masculine face, it was just as she thought it would be. His features were harsh from exposure and yet, like the outer covering of cloth he wore, the hollows beneath the cheekbones, the golden skin and wide, firm mouth were inherently, physically elegant. Perfect. The melted snow from his head dripped down the collar of his shirt, and his silk tie was askew. His hair was a thick, wavy sable color that, kept from a barber's ruthless control, might have curled and played around his ears.

And his eyes. Brown eyes. She'd thought they were dark. What she hadn't seen were the roughish glints of amber deep in the dark irises. Nor could she have guessed how they would crease with hustlerish fan lines when narrowed in amused speculation, as they were now, trained on her. Perfect. With the faintest shadow of a cleft in his strong, square chin.

Shelly possessed an innate appreciation for beauty, and the man in front of her was physically beautiful. She could also, when the situation arose, stand back and admire perfection.

She did not, however, covet either one.

She had dealt with perfect once before. From that experience she had learned a valuable lesson. Perfect men did not deal well with less-than-perfect situations. They weren't expected to know about the ups and downs in everyday life, and they had a tendency to flinch when things went bump in the night. She'd gleaned something else from the experience, but only after she'd been left bleeding.

Perfect was not just impossible to live up to, it had no conscious or soul.

Blinking, she pulled herself together and wryly finished her sentence of aeons ago, " . . . Fate."

Dan lost his train of thought, but it was replaced by the realization that he had to breathe sometime soon. Soft, was his first impression though he'd seen her strength, and familiar. Not pretty. *Pretty* was too innocuous a word. Certainly not beautiful. *Beautiful* was too tame to describe the small woman before him. The colors of her were incandescent, rose and gold flashing through copper hair, pastel blue-gray eyes blinking up from between spiked, russet lashes. Ivory skin, translucent, pale and baby fine, narrow nose, pointed chin . . . what big eyes she had.

Under the weight of her assessment, the grin he'd meant to charm her with slipped, then disappeared. It felt plastic and uncomfortable on his face. He wanted to ask if he passed the examination, but there was some quality in his examiner's expression that said he might not like the answer. It wasn't a look he was used to from a woman, and it caught him off guard.

"Or coincidence... yes, that's it." Shelly corrected herself conversationally, as if his eyes hadn't focused on her and lost all amusement, as if she wasn't stunned and could move at will, as if she could honestly take back the last thirty seconds. "It has to be coincidence. Why else would we both be traveling the same road, going to the same place at the same time?"

"What are you talking about?" Dan asked carefully. He didn't know what path she thought she was rambling down, but evidently he'd been left back at the stoplight. With a touch at her elbow, he urged her toward the counter. "Do I know you?"

He caught the glint of white teeth in her unexpected grin. "Never saw me before in your life," she told him, "but I've seen you." Turning to the waiting cashier, she ordered.

"Where...?" His tone was slow and measured.

"You're one of the famous 'cousins.'" Head down, Shelly fished in her coat pockets for the change to pay for the coffee. "That's what I meant about coincidence. I'm on my way up... to the homestead... your family place. Megan Sutherland insisted that I come tonight."

Dan was silent for a moment, watching Shelly pull out dimes and pennies, a pencil stub, two AA batteries, quarters and what looked to be several teardrop pearls embedded in a nest of lint. He could have reached into his own pocket and pulled out a bill large enough to pay for the coffeemaker itself, but he was too fascinated to think of it.

He cleared his throat. "Megan insisted you drive up tonight? That surprises me. It isn't like my aunt to insist on anything. Unless... are you a member of the wedding party?"

"I'm a worker, not a player."

"That tells me nothing."

In the act of shoving the excess coins and debris back into her pocket, Shelly paused and almost smiled. So spoke the, I-expect-you-to-tell-me-what-I-want-to-know-now-dammit, lordly male. That superior attitude again. If he didn't knock it off, she just might bite him.

"It means," she said slowly, reaching for her steaming cup, "something's happened your aunt can't deal with, and she wants it fixed tonight."

"You're on your way up to *fix* her problem?"

"If I can."

"In that case—" coffee in hand, Dan looked around for the closest empty table "—you'll have to drive more aggressively than you have been . . . if we want to get there any time soon. In fact, why don't I go ahead and finish out the trip."

Disbelief, then admiration played across Shelly's face, followed by an almost irresistible swell of laughter. She didn't deserve this. No one deserved this. The man had caught her flat-footed because, for some reason, she hadn't been expecting the predictable from him. She'd forgotten rule number five in the Prince Charming ethics code.

The tenet stated that there were certain men, and very few women, entitled to an assumptive arrogance. This attitude allowed them to discard or conveniently overlook minutiae or inconsequential facts. Dan Sutherland would, of course, own a copy of the manual.

It wasn't like Shelly to pick away at the small bits, but just who had rescued whom tonight, and why?

"You'll have to bear with me," she said, hiding behind big, solemn eyes, "because I think I'll go ahead and finish the trip at my own pace." She managed to control all but a hint of a smile. "Though I do appreciate the advice and the offer, it seems to me that *reaching* your aunt's house is more important than being quick. Rather than trying to conquer the highway, let's just keep the Bronco moving upon it."

Eyes narrowed, Dan considered how she stepped well back and angled her chin after delivering her shot. He was edgy and frustrated, and he just might have returned a jab if it hadn't been for that little chin. No street fighter would tilt it just so and then wait. A lady as tough as she pretended to be would have gone right for the jugular. Besides, Shelly was right. If he'd been paying closer attention, he would have known the semi had been going too fast to make the curve.

"Okay," he conceded, "the upper hand belongs to you this time...since I owe you for the ride home." His voice was mild, yet something quick and dark flashed in his eyes. "But watch out. Sooner or later, Shelly Barker, we'll be even."

## *Chapter Two*

Traffic inched through the renovated downtown district of Park City. Sidewalks and streets were clogged with ice-blown wind, and winter revelers, down from the slopes, were out to sample the night life of the once-infamous silver town. Once through, Shelly turned south onto a narrow road skirting a small valley, and then wound back up, higher behind the glittering lights and traffic. Turning again, the Bronco inched past an ice-encrusted iron gate that was normally locked, and clinked up a snow-packed lane for another quarter of a mile.

Pulling way over in the driveway, Shelly set the parking brake and left the engine running for warmth, then collapsed bonelessly over the steering wheel.

"You know, in the Chinese zodiac I'm a rooster." Her voice vibrated thin and shaky. "And we roosters are good for a lot of things. We always think we're right, and we usually are, and we're very interesting people. We do tend to put on a good act, though, when inside we're mush." Her fist pounded the dash with light, noiseless thuds. "I don't ever, ever, want to do that again."

Dan's voice was quietly insistent. "We're here, Shelly Barker. It's done. This time I'll buy the coffee. Hell, I'll grind the beans myself. Let's go in."

Shelly raised her head and looked around. Lights were on in the house. It was an old one, built much earlier in the century when vast porches, arches, balconies and stone turrets were the trademark of the day. There was character here, she decided, years of tears and triumph, generations of tales to be told. Despite cold stone and frigid snow, the windows spilled light and welcome. And people were waiting for her. She met Dan's gaze and nodded.

They were met at the door by a glassy-eyed, pale woman. It was, and yet was not, the same woman Shelly had left pleased and smiling four short weeks ago. Hunching her shoulders against the bite of the wind, Shelly stood back and let the nephew greet his aunt.

"Danny!" Megan Sutherland sputtered, throwing a harried glance down the driveway. "I-it's good to...is your...are they with you?"

No one else, Dan thought indulgently, but this one woman would dare. His own mother had never called him Danny. He bent his head and kissed the flushed, pink cheek. "Hello, Aunt Meggie. No, you did not make a mistake. The last time she and I traveled together, I nearly strangled Mother, so I decided to fly over early. She and Dad aren't due in until tomorrow, so calm down."

"I'd have worried myself sick if I had known you were coming up tonight—the weather reports have been nothing but horrendous. But I wish that you had called me. I'd have had you stop and pick up—"

"Shelly Barker?"

"Well, yes." The older woman blinked her confusion. "I was thinking of more ginger ale, but Shelly, too. How did you know?"

Because he wanted to, Dan bent to kiss his aunt's cheek a second time. "Would you believe *she* stopped to pick me up."

"Oh, my, they said cars were stranded up and down the canyon. Were you one of those, Danny?"

The overhang above the porch only provided a certain amount of protection from the needle-sharp cut of the wind. He would have welcomed the shelter and warmth inside the house, and he knew Shelly would, too, but in her excitement, his aunt had forgotten one thing: she had to let go of the door and move aside before they could step through. He did not, however, point that out. The more flustered Megan became, the greater the chance of frostbite. "If you let us in, we'll tell you about it." He kept his voice light and calm, "I promised Shelly—"

"She's here?" Megan Sutherland squeaked. "Of course, she's here... you just said so." Ducking around her nephew's broad shoulder, she saw Shelly and reached out to take her by the arm, pulling her into the house. "Thank goodness you're here. It's Debra, of course. I can't believe what she's done to herself, but she has. Do come in, Danny, and close the door. Did you bring your machine?" She threw the question over her shoulder as she headed toward the stairs in the center of the house.

Shelly followed up the steps to the first landing. She checked the urge to look back to make sure that Dan Sutherland stayed with her because... well, as insane as it was, she felt that since she had found him...she should keep him. The drive, she decided uneasily, must have cost her a whole lot of brain cells.

"It's out in my car," she said, answering Mrs. Sutherland's question. "What—what happened? What's wrong?"

"I'll tell you—utter chaos, that's what! Nerves, poor thing. What a time for her to go on a binge. She can't fit into her gown. I ask you, Shelly, how can we possibly have a wedding? We've sent out over five hundred invitations. What's going to happen when the guests get here and the bride can't squeeze into her wedding dress? She's in here."

Stopping at the third door along the plushly carpeted hall, Mrs. Sutherland placed her hand on the doorknob, hesitated, then whispered, "She been in her room crying ever since she tried the gown on this morning. If she isn't crying, she's eating. I'll tell you one thing, dear, I'll be so thankful when this wedding is over. My daughter is driving me right up the wall."

"How bad is it?" Shelly asked.

The older woman rolled her eyes and shuddered. "Bad."

Shelly did not like the sound of this, not one bit. Weeks of her life had gone in to the making of Debra Sutherland's wedding gown, countless hours spent hunched over, squinting as she hand sewed tiny crystal jets and seed pearls to the bodice and sleeves.

It was the most extravagant gown she had ever designed, and the price she'd charged reflected the time and effort spent in creation. But because Debra Sutherland had wanted such intricate handwork, and because she'd wanted the dropped heart waistline so snug there was only room left for *very* shallow breathing, an extra ounce could be fatal.

At the time, Shelly had cautioned Debra about that waistline. However, the client's name was Sutherland, and because Debra was spoiled and ultimately it was her gown and her money, Shelly had let it go.

Now she wanted nothing more than to gnash her teeth and tell Miss Have-it-your-own-way Sutherland, "I told you so." With a full commission to finish before Thanksgiving and her brother due to stay the entire week after, she didn't have time for this.

"Let's hope she makes it to the altar." There was a tiny catch in Mrs. Sutherland's voice. "The wedding is in four days. What if we can't fix it?"

Shelly stifled a sigh. The words and the wish for the daughter faded away under the mother's pleading glance. Mrs. Sutherland had never been anything but gracious and charming to Shelly. Besides, her professional pride demanded that Debra look magical in her gown, not blotched and mottled red from lack of oxygen. Of course, Shelly would do all she could.

With an absent glance down the hall, her gaze clashed with Dan Sutherland's brown one. He had followed at his own pace. He looked harmless, leaning against the wall, hands shoved deep into his trouser pockets, just as interested as he could be.

"You came all the way up here for a dress?" He sounded a bit incredulous. "At the very least, I thought we'd be having a ghost exorcized...or you'd come to fix the plumbing."

Snow melted off her hair and dripped down the back of Shelly's neck. Was it just her, or was this man simply becoming more irritating with time? And where, she wondered, did she hang up her coat once she got to take it off? "Debra is getting married in four days," she told him silky soft and reasonably. "It's a formal wedding. The bride is the focal point. Her gown needs to fit."

The gleam in his eyes could have meant anything, but if it was amusement as she suspected, he deserved a good, hard whack. Only an insensitive dolt would find this situation amusing.

With a smile dredged from the pit of her thoughts, Shelly dismissed the man and turned to Mrs. Sutherland. "Let me assess the damage and see what I can do."

"I knew I could count on you." The older woman's shoulders slumped with relief. "I knew you would help. There's so little time. You know, we have this entire week planned. The family arrives tomorrow." For a moment her thoughts appeared to travel down some unpleasant corridor, then she shook herself. "Shall we go in?"

Mrs. Sutherland looked as reluctant as she felt, but Shelly nodded her head. "Let's see what we're up against."

Debra Sutherland was sprawled across the huge, four-poster bed. When the light came on, she turned, snuffling pitiably. "Well, did the cavalry come?"

"She did," Shelly answered, stepping around the wads of used tissues littering the floor. From the look of it, Debra had been through boxes of the stuff. Her eyes were puffy from crying; her pale round face was blotched, streaked with mascara. Shelly's irritation turned to a wry sort of sympathy. Debra Sutherland looked about as miserable as it was possible for a privileged young woman to look.

"How bad is it?" Shelly asked quietly.

Debra's brown eyes swung to her mother, zoomed to the closet where the gown hung, then to Shelly. "Fourteen pounds," she whispered thickly, "and I've got one more wedding breakfast, two luncheons and two family dinners... all in the next four days. What am I going to do?"

Both mother and daughter were watching with such helpless expectancy, Shelly wanted to laugh. She advertised in the Yellow Pages as Dream Weaver, bringing romance and fantasy to life in the gowns she created. But not once, not ever, had she claimed to be a miracle worker. Nor had she ever claimed to be anyone's fearless leader, but drastic times called for drastic measures. Wiping her hand down the side of her pants, she squared her shoulders.

"First," Shelly began briskly, "we need to see where we stand. Then I'll bring in my machine. Somehow, we will salvage this."

Debra visibly perked up. "There you are, Mother. Shelly will fix it. It shouldn't be too hard."

This time it was more difficult to mask her irritation. Of course, she had sounded confident, Shelly thought. What else could she do at this point? Debra wasn't the one who was going to have to take off, then recenter the elaborately scalloped bead-and-appliqué work on the front and back panels of the bodice to adjust for those fourteen extra pounds. She wasn't the one taking the skirt and the stiff net of underskirt off to readjust the yards of heavy gathering, then sew it back on and redo the applique and beading to the new seams. Debra Sutherland merely had to wait for the cavalry to fix her problem, then walk down the aisle.

"So, Meggie?" Startled from her thoughts, Shelly turned at the sound of Dan's voice to find he had entered the room and was standing close behind her shoulder. "Where were you planning to put Shelly?"

"Put her?" Megan echoed, and bit her lip.

"Hmm, you weren't expecting her to drive back down the mountain tonight, were you? In this weather? Meggie?"

"Oh, dear." Myopic eyes skittered from Dan to Shelly. "I've been so caught up with caterers, musicians and such that I hadn't even thought about it. But you're right, Danny, how inconsiderate of me. Why, haven't we been listening to reports of the big accident in the canyon?" Her hands twisted, fluttered and fell. "I guess for tonight she can stay in the room next door. When the twins arrive, we'll—"

Dan went to his aunt and slipped a strong arm around her waist. "I know you're expecting a full house tomorrow, Meggie, and this wedding is making you crazy, but it's important to take care of Shelly Barker for as long as she's here." His eyes reached for Shelly's and held them with laughter. "Old Chinese proverb says, 'for the rescue of bleating buffalo, small rooster deserves sanctuary in warm, dry coop.'"

"That would be sheep." Shelly had to look away. She did not need to be taken care of, but the thoughtfulness expressed by his teasing words pierced her control and made it shaky. "Sheep bleat."

"Whatever." Dan shrugged. "Is there anything from the car you don't want brought in?"

"There are some things, yes. I'll walk out with you."

Dan left, but before she followed, Shelly had one last warning. "Debra, this is going to take time, and you'll have to help. Not one more pound. Even if I had the entire four days, there's only so much I can do."

For a moment it looked as though Debra Sutherland might snap at what was, after all, a mere dressmaker's audacity. In the next instant she must have decided against it. An almost sly glint turned her expression smug.

"I'll be good," she promised. "And think of the fun you're going to have. I know women who would kill to stay in the same house with the single Sutherland men . . . and you've already got Dan's attention." Her dark eyes narrowed. "Now that's interesting. Why, you're lucky I needed you to come up."

Shelly's first impulse was to laugh. Hysteria, she'd heard, was like that sometimes. Her next thought was to leave the room instantly, before the younger woman had a chance to really irritate her.

As she left, Shelly couldn't help wondering if Debra knew anything about living in the real world. Had she ever worked to support herself with no one else to do it for her? Did she know anything about responsibility? Obligations? Or was Debra's life, as a Sutherland Princess, so charming that she snapped her fingers and, poof, someone else always came in to handle the rough parts.

By eight o'clock the next morning, Shelly decided that was exactly what people did do for Debra Sutherland. Not because they wanted to, but to save sanity. Between delivery people, the UPS truck, the phone and the doorbell, Shelly lost track of time. And in a grand house that was supposedly filling to capacity, where was everyone?

"*OhmyGod,* it's the truck again," Debra would wail. "Shelly, can you get the door? I'm doing my nails. If it's another tea service, I'll scream. I mean, people don't even do the tea thing anymore, do they? Shelly?"

Right, Shelly thought, marching off to the door...again. Debra had a point. How much sterling silver did it take before the boundary of good taste was breached? She signed for, then deposited the package in the downstairs den with the rest of the tacky silver and gold.

"Shelly! It's the florist truck. Aunt Linda is coming in today and she absolutely demands fresh flowers in the house. You'll have to get the door. Mom's taken everyone out with her. What a time to leave me here, alone and helpless. Shelly?"

By nine-thirty, Shelly came to the conclusion that working in the room next to Debra's was not the solution to their mutual problem. Calmly packing up her sewing supplies, she waited until Debra disappeared into the bathroom, then took her portable machine and headed away from the bride-to-be.

How hard could it be, she wondered, to lose herself in a house the size of this one? Though not intimately familiar with it, she'd come to count four bedrooms and knew there were at least two levels she hadn't explored. This was a castle, after all—if nothing else, there had to be a dungeon.

Dan Sutherland was coming up the second landing as Shelly, lugging her machine, was going down. An unconscious smile touched his mouth as he hesitated, then came to a stop. The storm had blown east during the night and now sunshine coming through the cathedral-high entryway windows flooded the stairs with light. Her hair refracted colors until the glitter dazzled the eye, all the colors of last night and more, copper, ruby and orange.

He lowered his gaze to her burden for a long minute, then up to her face. The clue to her mood was the way she held the machine. And the spit in her glare as she stared right back at him stretched his smile to a grin. Something in the rigidity of her stance told him that if he was fool enough to extend his hand, he'd be pulling it back minus fingers.

"I thought sure you would have lasted longer," he said mildly. "Oh, well, I don't think Aunt Megan will hold a grudge too long. If she wasn't the mother of the bride, she'd probably bail out with you. Can I get you anything before you go? An aspirin?"

Temper moved impatiently through Shelly. This morning, Prince Dan Charming looked lazy and primed, barefoot, with his hair slightly mussed. Long-legged temptation in white, tight jeans and a navy blue T-shirt. Sure, he could afford to tease the hired help. He had four days of gala wedding festivities to look forward to. She had at least sixteen hours of alterations and . . . Debra.

"I am not leaving. What I'm doing is looking for a—" Racking her brain, she could not think of one tactful word to describe what she wanted.

Dan nodded with sudden understanding. "You're looking for a place to hide?"

"Somewhere away from the family. I've got hours of handwork to do . . . I may have to stay another night." The machine was getting heavy and she didn't care if she sounded desperate. "Is there such a place?"

"Well—" his tone altered, deepened "—there is a small, self-contained apartment off the kitchen—bedroom, bath . . . even a sitting room where you could spread out."

"Perfect!" Shelly shifted the weight in her arms. She had been looking for a quiet corner, but hadn't expected anything as unique as a suite. "It sounds perfect."

"No objection to being exiled that far away from the family? When we were kids—" he bent closer "—we 'cousins' used to lock each other up down there... for hours, alone.... We called it the servant's dungeon."

She refused to let the naughty-boy smile in his brown eyes distract her. "I won't mind being on my own."

"I didn't think you would," he said with deceptive innocence, "but luckily you won't have to be. You see, when I'm in town, I always get first dibs on the dungeon. The apartment is mine. But since I still feel as if I owe you something for last night's rescue, I'm willing to move over and share." He shrugged. "And if you have to spend another night, well, I'm sure we can find an extra pillow somewhere."

Though his comment was obnoxious, she could have let it pass... if he hadn't started grinning. Her eyes narrowed as she considered dropping the machine on his bare feet, except that he was standing several steps below her and she didn't think the thirty odd pounds would bounce that far. "You are," she said between clenched teeth, "an incredible man."

"Thank you." He wondered how much more he could get away with before she erupted from simmer to flash. The annoyance in her eyes pleased him. Even after she'd had a night to sleep on the merits of charming a Sutherland versus biting one, Shelly looked ready to fight. He liked that.

"But, no, thank you," she was saying as she half turned away. "You keep your cozy little torture chamber... and your pillow. I'll go back and take my chances with Debra."

Dan stopped her midhuff by simply stepping up, backing her against the wall and pinning her there with his hands on her shoulders. He had the advantage, because she held the machine. Towering above her, he bent his head so close, he could have counted the golden freckles across her nose, could have given her an Eskimo kiss.

"You misunderstand me." His hands slid slowly from her shoulders, down her arms to her elbows. "I only meant you could have my bed if it looked like you were staying another night." His hands slid lower, slower, stopping for a moment to feel the quick, fluttery pulse in her wrists. "While I, of course, take my pillow and bunk upstairs with a cousin." She shivered, he felt it and looked her honestly in the eye. "If that's what I have to do."

Shelly, to her everlasting surprise, had to drop her gaze before she could answer. "You do."

"Fair enough," Dan said, and he plucked the sewing machine from her hands. "For now."

Turning, he led the way down two flights of stairs to the back of the house. "I'll dig up a worktable or whatever else you need, then I'm out of here for a while." He opened a door on the far side of the kitchen and reached for the light switch. "And, Shelly, if I were you, I'd steer clear of the incoming relatives, especially the female ones. There is one that can be . . . temperamental."

Later in the afternoon, Shelly was frantically wondering where Dan had gotten the harmless description. Funny how she'd known right off that Linda Sutherland was the woman he'd been referring to. To say that the other Mrs. Sutherland, from the Denver branch of the family, was temperamental was rather like saying Ivan the Terrible was a bit testy.

The first volley blasted immediately upon her arrival. A softly sweet, imperious voice drifted down from the upstairs landing. "Megan? Oh, Megan, dear? I'm simply famished after the flight over." Tea was then requested . . . to be taken upstairs . . . with a light broth and perhaps one of those marvelous little crullers from the bakery on Park City's main street.

Shelly had happened to be in the kitchen with Megan Sutherland at the time. In the process of assembling a lunch tray with dainty finger sandwiches and coffee, the older woman had looked up, so helplessly distraught that Shelly immediately went for her own car keys.

The next thing Shelly knew, she had been pressed into service. It wasn't that she resented being asked to unpack the three cases of designer clothes, hanging them away in the spacious walk-in closet. At another time she would have admired the workmanship and enjoyed handling the expensive fabrics of the exclusive labels. What she did resent was the instruction to press nonexistent wrinkles from the garments before putting them away. She had not come up the mountain to act as ladies' maid.

Matters were not helped along when Megan Sutherland reported to Shelly that she and Debra were leaving to meet the groom and his parents.

"Just you and Debra?" Shelly's normally quiet voice rose in horror. "What about the other Mrs. Sutherland?" *What about the wedding gown? What about the possible assault charge if I'm left alone with the tyrant upstairs?*

"I'm sorry, dear," Megan said, worrying her lip between her teeth. She did look sorry. In fact, she looked close to collapse. "I've asked my sister-in-law to come with us, but she insists upon waiting for our husbands to get back from the airport with her daughters. I don't know why they couldn't have all come together." Her shrug was resigned and her gaze automatically traveled upward. "Yes, I do, too. As for my boys, Ty and Kiall... no doubt they're with their Cousin Dan. As youngsters, those three were known as the Terrible Trio, and they haven't changed. They knew about this banquet, you bet they did, but until we find them, the only thing Debra and I can do is go ahead and represent the family."

This was it, Shelly decided rebelliously, the ultimate betrayal of trust, the final exploitation of her good nature. They honestly meant to leave her alone and, heaven help her, at the mercy of the Wicked Witch of the East.

"Shelly? I know you're here. Answer me, Shelly Barker!"

Oh, no, Shelly thought in panic, not again. Ice cubes, mud packs, herb tea and crackers, fingernail-polish remover, rubber bands and extra towels. What now? It was getting closer—The Voice. Could this woman do nothing for herself?

Shelly had been discovered in the servant's dungeon first thing. For a while she'd been safe hiding out in Debra's room. Then she'd tried working on the utility porch, but it had been too cold to stay out there for long. The Voice had driven her upstairs and down, from one end of the castle to the other. Eventually, though, relentlessly, The Voice found every one of her hiding places.

"Ms. Barker? I insist you answer immediately, or I shall report your insolence to Megan."

And then what, Shelly questioned wildly, I'm fired? She had been paid for the gown's completion over four weeks ago and, as yet, there had been no talk of what she could expect in the way of remuneration for her extra time now. Anyway, even when the subject did come up, no amount of money was worth this aggravation.

The Voice loomed closer.

Shelly knew she could not get back upstairs. She also knew that if she headed to the small sitting room where her supplies were located, she'd be had. Her desperate gaze swung around the kitchen, selecting then eliminating options.

The bathroom? Yes, there was universal sanctuary in a bathroom. It was an unwritten law, by God probably, and strictly upheld by civilized man.

Figuring that she had less than forty seconds until The Voice pounced, Shelly slithered stealthily toward safety. Her breath came in short, panicky puffs. Under her hand the door opened on a soundless click. She slipped inside, turning as she did so to close it and ram the locking bolt home.

Safe! She said the word again, out loud, resting her forehead against the closed panel. "I'm safe," she whispered fiercely, pounding her fist soundlessly against the wood. "I'm leaving," she decided. "Of all the obnoxious, overbearing, arrogant—" She ran out of dictionary words. Taking a shallow breath, she dredged for more graphic descriptives. Plenty came to mind. "Bitchy... witchy... first Debra... then her."

"Dare I need ask... her whom?"

This voice was mellow, mildly curious, and she knew it.

Shelly whirled. Her startled gaze took in Dan's bareback, barefoot frame and registered his half-lathered face as he stood poised, razor held midair, staring back at her in the mirror. His hair was damp, and she could smell the moisture and soap freshness on his bare skin from his very recent shower. The loose material of his drawstring sweats draped low over the firm globe of his left bare buttock as he calmly leaned again to the mirror and took another swipe at his face with the razor.

"I thought you were gone." It wasn't much, but it was the best she could do.

"I came back. Meggie has some kind of fancy party planned tonight, a dinner I think, black tie." He rinsed the collected foam off the razor. "Let's get back to the arrogant... overbearing *her.*" His smile was slow and lazy and just a touch malicious. "You wouldn't be speaking of my dear old mum, would you, Shelly?"

## *Chapter Three*

Shelly realized what she had done. With a strangled gasp, her nose was immediately back into the wood of the door, so firmly entrenched, there was danger of splinters.

"Just who are we discussing?" Dan prodded.

A pounding began on the other side of the door. "Shelly? Ms. Barker? I know you're in there. Of course, you are in there. I demand that you come out."

"Ah," a deep exaggerated sigh of enlightenment came from the man behind her. The banging grew more imperious. He took his time, splashing water on his face to rinse away the last of the shaving cream.

Shelly kept perfectly still. She knew she had made more than one tactless blunder in the last sixty seconds. Silently, she cursed fate, her simple mind and her big mouth. As yet, she hadn't met Debra's brothers, but Dan was not one of them. Dan was not from this area. He'd flown in yesterday. Oh, yes, Shelly realized what she had done. Not only had she grossly invaded his privacy, but she had all but blasphemed Dan's—

"I happen to be in here," Dan called over the sound of running water.

"Dan? What in the world are you doing? Why didn't you answer me?"

"I'm doing," he drawled, setting his bottle of after-shave aside and casually reaching over and flushing the toilet, "what one would assume I'd be doing . . . Mother."

That's right, Shelly thought with a dull lurch of her stomach. The woman banging on the other side of the door was this man's mother. Shelly couldn't move. It didn't matter. Any moment now, Dan would give her some assistance, a helping shove right out the door.

"Dan," his mother called out, "don't be cute. Of course, I know what you're doing. What I meant was, I expected someone else to be in there."

Shelly held her breath. This was it, no use trying to explain why she had locked herself in the bathroom with the cousin from Denver. Why should anyone believe her?

Though she heard no footsteps or noise, Shelly knew exactly when Dan moved to stand behind her. She could feel him close in the subtle shift of the room's energy, felt his sudden, radiant heat at her back. His scent alone was enough to make a staunch heart skip and flutter.

"Who would that be, Mother?"

"The maid, of course. You *are* in the servants suite. Your aunt hired her to help out through the wedding. My guess is, Megan didn't bother to check for references." The well-bred snort of irritation could be heard through the door. "Really, Dan, I'm not going to stand here yelling. When you're finished, please come up and see me. Also, if you see the red-headed girl, send her up. If I were Megan, I'd send that sly little madam packing."

Unaware of the receding footsteps, Shelly's mind grappled with the situation. *Sly little madam!* She wondered if there was a way to get even instead of just mad, and decided there probably was not.

"You can turn around now."

Surprised by the whispered conspiracy she heard in Dan's voice, Shelly considered the offer. "No, thank you," she said politely, groping for the lock.

"I wouldn't go out just yet if I were you," his whisper came again. "My guess is she's hovering just outside the kitchen door...waiting to pounce. It's an old trick of hers."

The small thump between Shelly's eyes spread, banding, tightening around her skull. She put a hand up to massage it loose. This was, she thought on a long sigh, a damnable day.

"Headache?" His whisper softened with compassion. "My mother has that affect on people."

"Yes, no... it isn't all her," Shelly murmured honestly. "I stayed up very late last night. Do you have any idea what it's like, nodding off face first into piles of crystal?"

Dan stared at the thin back presented to him. His alarm grew when her shoulders began to move suspiciously under the voluminous material of her flannel shirt. His mother had a knack for pushing people to the edge. Maybe she had pushed Shelly Barker right over the cliff.

If Shelly hadn't been hit by a sudden fit of laughter, she would have turned around to look at Dan Sutherland. *Red-headed girl?* The toilet flush had been inspired. No wonder he was the tiniest bit... off center. She appreciated the fact that he could keep his mouth shut. And she very much liked the humor she'd heard in his voice. His sense of ridiculous made this situation absurd rather than embarrassing.

Dan touched her shoulder, still whispering, "Are you laughing or crying?"

Shelly chewed her bottom lip for a moment. "I don't know yet." She didn't mind his hand on her shoulder, but she didn't quite understand the odd note in his voice. Curious, she turned around and tipped back her head. "Which should I be?"

Dan blinked his surprise. Those weren't tears in her pastel blue eyes, simply the glittering residue of laughter. He made a deprecating sound between his teeth. "Since my mother has been known to make the strong weep, I wasn't sure which way you'd swing."

Then he went silent and stared at Shelly thoughtfully for a full ten seconds. "Without me here," he murmured at last, his head angling to one side and bending close, "she'd have nailed you." He was so close, his breath brushed the fine hair at her temple. "Would that be a fair assessment, Shelly?"

Silence spun out. Why, she wondered suspiciously, was he asking, like that, with his voice dropped to a dark, lazy drawl? She would concede to a certain amount of overreaction, and she was, for all intents, hiding out behind a locked door, but she was not a child. This would have been easier if he was wearing something more than a pair of loose-fitting sweats.

"Fair-enough." Now she understood why narrow hips, long legs and chest hair caused some women to stutter, "S-so?"

"So?" Bracing his hand on the door behind her head, he bent his own until less than an inch separated the curl of his lashes from the spiky tips of hers. Until he could see behind the flicker of unease in her eyes, feel the soft, uneven puff of her breath against his skin and was satisfied that she was every bit as aware as he. "I figure all debts are paid. That makes us even."

"How can we be even when you keep bailing me up against walls and doors?"

"Oh, you mean this?" The grin on his mouth and in his eyes pushed those fan-line creases into prominence and, if the face he pulled was playful, the soft, slow draw of his thumb against her jaw line was not. "I've decided I like holding you captive against hard surfaces, Shelly Barker. It makes me feel primal and macho and...hairy. Besides, how else am I going to get your attention?"

Shelly would have pushed at him if she had been more sure she could touch his bare chest and get her hand to move away. But what woman wouldn't be shaking inside? Dan Sutherland possessed the same fantasy value for a single woman as any Prince Charming would. When Cinderella came along, she was bound to get a deal. As for Shelly, she wasn't much for fantasy unless it was in the gowns she created.

She could have chosen better words. But because she did not like the way he kept pushing, she chose to be blunt. "Stick to playing in your own sandbox, Dan. You'd have to learn a whole new set of rules for mine."

Something flickered in his eyes, and his question was slow and quiet. "Are you trying to tell me to back off?"

"You've got it."

"Uh-uh, I don't think so." Dropping his hand, he stepped back. "But give me a few minutes to finish dressing, and I'll speak to my mother about it."

Shelly had almost forgotten what brought her into this room. "No, thank you. She thought I was the maid, here to help with the wedding. Now that I know what her problem is, I'll speak to your mother myself."

That stopped him. Dan's hand paused in the act of swinging the door open for her. "*She* has the problem? You're the one hiding out in the bathroom!"

"May I come in?"

Startled, the needle in her hand missed the tiny hole in the seed pearl, jamming itself into Shelly's finger instead. With a grimace, she glanced up to see the mother of the bride peering through the open door. Nodding, Shelly motioned Megan Sutherland in. "Please."

"Dan told me about the showdown this afternoon. You must have handled it fairly well." Megan laughed. "You're still alive to talk about it."

At first Shelly thought they must be talking about her tactless blunder into the bathroom. Then she realized Megan was referring to the small skirmish she had had with the other Mrs. Sutherland.

Shelly wouldn't say that she had been the outright victor in that battle. Mrs. Linda Sutherland had not been pleased to have her mistake pointed out. In fact, so much displeasure had gone into the haughty, "I see" that Shelly had checked for footprints on her backside after she'd been shown the door. But since the confrontation, she had been left alone.

After checking to make sure she hadn't pricked herself enough for blood to get on the gown, she shook out the folds of fabric spread across her lap and held up the bodice for inspection. "I think we may have it...maybe not finished tonight, but definitely by tomorrow."

"Oh." For a moment it looked as though Megan Sutherland might cry. "I'm so glad. I had a dream last night that my daughter walked down the aisle in a brown paper bag."

Shelly's eyes widened with sympathy. "Good grief."

"That's not the worst part," Megan said, moving farther into the room. She bent her head confidingly closer and lowered her voice. "The worst of it was when her Aunt Linda leapt from her seat, knocked down the minister and began stomping through the wedding cake, shouting, 'I told them brown was a bad color!'"

Shelly's breath caught on a sudden laugh. "That must have been some dream."

Megan nodded solemnly. "A nightmare," she agreed. Reaching out to touch one of the glittering crystals, she gave Shelly a sudden, thoughtful look. "You've been at this for hours. Have you had anything to eat?"

Shelly tried to remember. "I think I had something about three."

"Do you know what time it is now? It's after twelve. Oh, dear, this is my fault...with the luncheon this afternoon and the family dinner this evening, I simply forgot all about you."

"Mrs. Sutherland," Shelly said calmly, positioning another pearl, "I'm in the room next to your kitchen." She pushed the needle in and carefully drew the silk thread out. "And unless you have your refrigerator padlocked, I'll raid when I get hungry."

"Promise?"

Shelly looked up from her work, smiling. "Oh, I promise. Since I live alone, I'm not much for routine—" she shrugged "—but when I'm hungry, I eat."

"I wish Debra were more like you...at least until after this wedding is over. I've had to watch her all day." Megan hesitated then said, "I'm wondering, Shelly, if... No, I hate to ask you."

"What is it, Mrs. Sutherland?"

"Oh, it's just that the kitchen is, as you say, right next door, and if Debra should happen to come downstairs while you are working, could you...?"

"Guard her waistline with my life?" Shelly guessed at the unspoken request.

Still Megan hesitated. "I've asked so much of you already. Do you mind?"

Since Shelly had arrived in the Sutherland household, she had acted as telephone receptionist, package handler, delivery person, drudge and lady's maid. Hours had gone into altering the wedding gown. She'd suffered irritation, frustration and aggravation. The least, she thought, the very least she could do to get down off the blasted mountain was guard the refrigerator. "No," she assured Mrs. Sutherland, "I don't mind."

"If you're sure. Everyone is in for the night...and really, I don't expect any trouble. Debra promised to be good." She stopped at the door. "Please, dear, don't stay up much later."

"Just a bit longer," Shelly said, hedging. Just as long as it took to finish. "Good night, Mrs. Sutherland."

Minutes—or hours—later, Shelly raised her eyes from the half-blurred lines of bead work. The door had been left ajar and, although it was dark and quiet in the kitchen, she knew someone was in there.

She laid the dress aside. With one reckless dash already behind her, she wasn't about to go blustering into the unknown again. The luck she seemed to be having would put one of the Sutherland men in the kitchen. This time, she thought, it would be more diplomatic to check before she charged. She switched off the table lamp and stood up. Now both rooms were in darkness. Putting a hand up to feel the way, she walked quietly.

The refrigerator door hung wide open, spilling the only light into the room, casting faint patterns on the walls and tiled floors. The dim light illuminated, yet still shrouded Debra Sutherland in shade and shadow.

Undecided, Shelly stood well back. Now that it had come to a showdown, she wasn't sure how to proceed. Did she cock her imaginary six-shooter and order Debra to drop the loot? Or would a flying body tackle be more effective? She was about to announce herself when another form joined Debra's in front of the refrigerator.

"Debra? What are you doing up so late?" The voice was quiet and deep, one to take comfort from in the hushed stillness of a troubled night.

"I can't sleep."

"What's bothering you?"

Debra's voice trembled, "Oh, Dan!"

Unwittingly, Shelly was caught in the unfolding scene. She caught the instant Debra's cousin opened his arms to catch and support Debra as she threw herself, sobbing, against him.

Again, Shelly Barker found herself guilty of invading Dan Sutherland's privacy. The first time had been an accident. This time she had trespassed deliberately. She remained silent, a witness as the one light silhouetted the tenderness of the man to the woman.

"Oh, Dan, I'm so scared," Debra cried softly.

"Is that what this is all about?" he asked gently, bending his head protectively over Debra's. He put a hand on her hair, holding her patiently as her sobs wet the front of his shirt. "Easy, little cousin," he murmured after a while. "You have to stop. You're hurting yourself."

"I can't seem to help it." Debra's voice was scratchy. "I know this—" she waved toward the open refrigerator "—isn't helping, but I don't know what else to do. I think, what if Paul—" Her voice broke. "W-what if he decides he can't deal with the family, after all. You know what we're like. And then I think... what if he's only marrying me because my name is Sutherland?"

Long moments passed. Dan continued to stroke her hair until she was calm. "There's no option when it comes to choosing family, Deb, but you can choose your friends. And I also believe that a person has options when it comes to loving. Has Paul told you he loves you?"

"Y-yes," came the hesitant, whispered reply.

"Do you believe him?"

"Yes, I do... I want to."

"Then I guess when it comes down to the crunch all any of us can do is take it on faith." Dan's voice was a quiet, reflective rumble and while he searched for an answer to give Debra, he absently rubbed his cheek against her hair. "You can't change the family or who you are. So if you love Paul enough to marry him, you'll have to trust that it's you he wants and that he can deal with the rest of us."

Debra looked up. "Is it that simple, Dan?"

He opened his mouth, closed it, then shook his head. "Beats me," he admitted gruffly. "If it's not, it should be." Giving Debra a quick, hard hug, he put her away from him. "Now, are we going to have this party?"

"No." Debra managed a watery giggle, "I'm going back upstairs."

"Sure? One last raid together before you become an old married woman?"

"I'm sure," Debra said. "You stay here and eat. I've got a wedding in three days." She hesitated. "Dan?"

"What is it?"

"Just... thanks."

"Anytime," Dan called after her retreating figure.

Silence filled the kitchen. The image of what she'd seen was with Shelly as she dragged a shallow breath into her lungs. The shadow of a large, strong hand stroking a fragile, bent head remained sharply imprinted. The aching echo of whispered acceptance and concern shimmered in the still room.

The scene lingered. The tenderness of it left her humbled, awed by its generosity. The beauty of it sharply clarified the dull ache she'd felt in her own heart lately. It focused on and made her aware of the lack of intimacy in her own life.

Before she could move, before her frozen feet could obey the directive from her numbed brain to get out, Dan located the sound of her ragged breathing and turned in her direction.

"Is that you, Shelly? Are you coming or going?"

"I'm sorry."

Her hand went to her mouth as a second light was switched on. The small light above the range was not bright enough to disturb the night, but sufficient to reveal the sheen of tears in her wide, startled eyes. Bright enough to illuminate her distress.

Two emotional women in one night? Dan had dealt with the first because she was family. He was under no obligation to acknowledge awareness of the second. She gave him an out, keeping well back into the shadow of the door.

But what, he wondered, had put the gloss of tears in Shelly Barker's eyes? Why had her small, triangular face gone so pale, it was noticeable in the semidarkness? How had anything said in the past few minutes hurt her enough to make her cry? He could have let the moment pass. It would have been enough to make some remark and get out of the kitchen. Instead he took a step toward her. "Why are you sorry?"

"For eavesdropping. This seems to be my day for intruding." Her voice was husky. "I'm sorry about this afternoon and now. I don't know why I didn't leave."

Dan knew as surely as if someone whispered it over his shoulder that it took a lot to make this woman cry. He'd seen independence in her refusal to let him fight the battle with his mother. There had been stubbornness in the mental squaring of her shoulders when it came to getting a job done and strength in her march as she had gone, unhesitantly, off to war. Humor danced when she grinned, and her gaze was honest in its admiration of him as a man.

Dan couldn't say why, but it unsettled him to think that he'd somehow pierced the armor of this fragile little warrior.

"Come help me raid the refrigerator." The request was out before the thought completed itself in his mind. "And I'll forgive you."

Shelly managed a smile, asking the same question Debra had. "Is it that simple?"

"Sure it is," Dan said, then chuckled. "Come on, let's see what goodies Aunt Megan has stashed away."

Shelly was still feeling odd aftershocks. Sporadic tremors trembled through different muscles in her body. Tears continued to blur her vision. She understood that he was trying to make this easy for her, and her estimation of him underwent yet another change.

"Thank you, no," she said quietly, and turned to fade back into the dungeon room. It was late and she was tired. Until she regained her balance, it would be safer to keep her distance.

"Please? A midnight feast isn't the same without someone to share it with. I'll cook."

Wistfully, Shelly looked over her shoulder. She *was* hungry, and tomorrow she'd be gone. Would it hurt to spend just a few more minutes with this man? she asked herself. *Besides all the time he's had in your thoughts? Maybe,* came the immediate reply. She had promised Megan that she would eat—when, two hours ago? He's only asked to share her company so he wouldn't have to eat alone. She could handle that much. Couldn't she?

The truth was, although Shelly knew it would mean trouble, she wanted to stay. She knew she shouldn't, but her guard was down. Earlier, in the bathroom, she had granted her hormones full overdrive permission. After all, a woman would have to have been past all coherent thought to ignore the smooth, muscled flesh less than an inch from her nose. Those feelings were controllable; they were human.

Now, she admitted, it was more than Dan's pretty face and hard body that pulled her closer. She hadn't wanted to be charmed by him. Hadn't considered that she could be. She'd been wrong.

"Is it because I'm my mother's son?" Dan checked his step toward her. The novelty of the situation pricked his sense of humor. "I don't think it's fair of you to hold her eccentricities against me."

Shelly exhaled slowly and felt the muscles of her shoulders relax. A reluctant smile lifted her mouth. "No," she agreed, "that would not be fair. I know all about eccentric relatives. Remember when I mentioned my brother?" She tugged at the hem of her shirt. Compared to her brother, the demanding Mrs. Linda Sutherland was as mild as milk and sugared coffee. "He has some unique personality quirks of his own."

"Then we have something in common." The brown of Dan's eyes warmed with sharp amusement. "If we discuss it, we might find something else."

"You're not going to try the primal, flat-surface trick again, are you?"

"I can't promise."

She had mistakenly discounted his good humor. When life ran on smooth cogs, it was easy enough to smile. The test, she knew, came when the machine broke down. What she hadn't taken into account was how beguiling a smile could be, how much she wanted to trust... to believe it.

Shelly didn't expect the warmth that Dan had given to his cousin, but he was willing to share his company. For a small space in time, he would be there, someone to smile with, to talk to in the middle of the night.

Solitude surrounded them. The flash of his white grin beckoned. He was a smooth one, this man. Dangerous. Even though she knew better, his company was too tempting. Shelly moved reluctantly into the kitchen.

"What's on the menu?"

## *Chapter Four*

"Ah," Dan murmured, unprepared to admit that he had been holding his breath. "Whatever madam wishes." He pulled a chair away from the heavy oak table and made a sweeping gesture for Shelly to be seated. "I recommend the house special this evening."

Uttering a sigh, Shelly glanced up at him as she sat. The corner of her mouth rose. "What *is* the house special?"

"You will have to trust me on this," Dan intoned solemnly. "Let an older, much wiser gourmand be your guide."

"My digestion is in your hands," she said, curious to see what he would come up with.

Dan didn't often play the fool, but in the muted hush of the sleeping house, he found he didn't mind. Not when it replaced Shelly's tears with a shy, dancing laugh. Not when the soft brush of her gaze smiled on him as he moved from cabinet to table.

He laid the table with two frill-edged placemats he found in a drawer. Lead-crystal wine goblets came down from the top shelf, along with gold-handled cutlery from his aunt's display case. The deep bowls he placed on the mats were of the finest china, and he went back to the drawer to find linen napkins. When a match had been lighted to the fat, green candle centerpiece unearthed from a back shelf, he stood back.

"Well," he prompted, "is madam pleased?"

"It's all very nice," Shelly murmured gravely, "especially the Christmas candle. It's just that..."

"Yes?"

"I believe there was mention of food."

"Of course." Dan snapped his fingers and stepped briskly to the cabinet, then the refrigerator.

When he finally took a chair next to her, Shelly blinked at the feast presented on the table. Laughter bubbled close to the surface. "My compliments to the chef."

"You will notice," Dan said, tipping the box of Cocoa Puffs so the brown nuggets pinged into her bowl, "a subtle blending of flavor and texture. This dish happens to be one of the finest culinary triumphs of the century." He reached for the milk carton. "Is there anything else madam wishes before we begin?"

Wine bubbled in the crystal goblets. The smell of chocolate blended with the scent of the bayberry candle, and underlying all was the elusive scent of the man's musky aftershave. Shaking out her napkin, Shelly picked up her spoon. "Everything," she announced quietly, "is perfect."

The third time she caught Dan staring, Shelly gave the cereal in her mouth a final crunch, swallowed and set her spoon down. "All right," she said, sighing in resignation, "I suppose we've known each other long enough now to get personal. Let's get this over with. Yes, it's natural, there is a lot of it, and it is orange."

Dan dropped his eyes. "What are you talking about?"

Because she was feeling less shaky, stronger within herself, Shelly could give him a frank, teasing smile. "We're talking about my hair. Every time I've looked up, you've been staring. It's okay, you know. This color just happens to run in my family."

"It's not orange," Dan said slowly, trying to decide what color he would call it. Dark marmalade was the best he could do.

As he continued to study the subject and ponder, the color rose in Shelly's cheeks and she looked away. He nudged the spoon back into her hand. She didn't eat nearly enough, he thought suddenly. Three bites and she was done? No wonder she was so thin. "This morning, when we met on the stairs? Do you remember?"

Unconsciously, Shelly tipped her head to one side. She remembered, of course. She remembered. She had not been able to hold her hands steady for minutes afterward. "Yes."

"The stairs had been flooded with light. I swear I saw sparks." Dan set his own spoon down and gave her a long, level stare. "When I touched you, there was nothing to you, no flesh on your bones, nothing but hair and big eyes. Just for an instant, you seemed too insubstantial to be real."

Shelly returned his look, stare for stare. "You can," she said at last, "get professional help for most anything these days."

"Hey, I'm being sincere." He tried for a hurt look. "Do you always give men such a hard time?"

Shelly kept a straight face, barely. "The last man I listened to was his most sincere after several glasses of wine." Her eyes narrowed suspiciously. "How much did you have to drink at Debra's dinner party tonight?"

Dan tipped back his head and laughed. Lifting his wineglass, he touched it to Shelly's. "My first and only glass today," he told her.

Odd, he hadn't been able to concentrate on much today except Shelly Barker. Truth was, since returning from Debra's dinner party, he'd had trouble settling. He hadn't been able to sleep, and feeling restless, he had come downstairs to prowl. The impact of finding Shelly there in the shadows had been something like a swift, hard jab to the chest.

Dan draw the glass to his lips. The wine wasn't nearly as tempting to him as she was and, setting the drink aside, he did what he'd been wanting to do all day. He reached out to see if the copper in her hair was as fiery as it looked.

It was the strangest thing, but once he had his hand out, he found himself reaching for the curve of her face to trace the three amber freckles placed high across her cheekbone. The pad of this thumb found the ones splashed across her small, straight nose, and he discovered that her skin was as smooth as he had imagined it to be, but much softer.

At the first brush of his fingers, Shelly went quiet. During their earlier encounters, he had, more or less, held her captive, and because of that, she'd been able to brace herself against the friction building between them. Dan sensed she wasn't much less determined now, but this time it was what she felt that held her still.

With his thumb he traced the fragile outline of her jaw before he tangled with the hair flowing around her shoulders. The texture was finer than he imagined. It slid through his fingers, cool and silky. Under the table, her hands were clasped tightly together, but they were the only part of her reaction she thought to hide. The rest of it—her curiosity about him, the pleasure his hands seemed to give as they stroked and probed—were there for Dan to see.

A sigh swelled in his chest. He wanted her to hide what she felt. It would have been easier for him, safer for her. His fingers refused to leave the satiny, shampoo-scented strands.

"Mr. Sutherland?" Foolishly, Shelly thought to inject some distance in the situation by addressing Dan formally. She succeeded only in sounding stuffy, stiff and ridiculous. Her heart beat fast and furious in her chest while her blood thrummed and pulsed through her body. What she wanted was to wrap around him and purr. "I don't think this is a good idea."

"I think we know each other intimately enough for you to call me Dan. The rule on that one is . . . once you've seen a man in low-hung sweats and shaving cream, you may then address him by his Christian name."

Even as the nonsense fell from his mouth, Dan found himself wondering what she would call him if he took her through to the small bedroom and touched her exactly how and where the impulse moved him. He dropped his gaze from hers and forced his hand away.

Despite what he had just done, Dan was not a casual toucher. In his personal life, he preferred women with a polished style, an emotional veneer, a certain degree of sophistication. Shelly Barker had exchanged her red flannel shirt of the morning for a gray one for the evening. Not much style in flannel this season, he guessed, and if she had any sophistication, she kept it well hidden. As for veneer, hers was eggshell thin.

As he continued to study the disarming woman, looking into eyes that were wide and dilated, Dan experienced the same disorientation he'd felt that morning on the stairs. A sensation not unlike a blow to the head; no pain, but just as stunning. "I'm not usually this..." He searched for a word to explain his behavior.

"How does *impetuous* sound? Or *Rash?* Or *pushy?* Or—"

"Try *intrigued.*"

A startled, what-in-heaven's-name-are-you-saying look came into her eyes. It was a child-alarmed, woman-bewildered expression. And with it, every trite, practiced line Dan had ever said, every skilled, experienced maneuver he ever made slipped from his mind. "No," he said, answering the question for both of them, "I don't know what I'm doing."

He had two choices. One, he could pack away the Cocoa Puffs and hightail it upstairs to sanity. That would be the sensible, rational decision. Or two, he could ignore common sense and stay right where he was. All his life Dan had taken pride in being a rational, logical man. With extreme courtesy, he sat back in his chair. "Are you finished?"

Shelly was surprised to find the bowl still on the table. For a few brief moments, the only thing in the room had been Dan Sutherland. She gave a short, jerky nod. Yes, she thought, she was finished. Her chair scraped against the tile as she pushed back. Thinking hard, she sifted through the past few minutes, looking for just the right perspective to slot them into.

After-midnight fantasy encounters were great things, she finally decided. Every woman deserved at least a memory of one to take out and polish or embellish as winter piled snow high against her door. But they weren't real.

The important thing was to know fact from fiction.

"I'll finish straightening up," she offered, and she even managed a smile. "You did the cooking."

Choices. Options. A man had them; he lived with those he made. With this woman, Dan discovered he didn't want to settle for a touch when a taste was so close. He honestly had no inkling of what he was going to do until it happened. When Shelly Barker reached over to collect his bowl, he reached for Shelly Barker.

His hands were gently insistent, pulling her closer. Had he been demanding, Shelly would have refused strictly on principal. There was a look to him that said he was as bemused as she. This could, she thought, get tricky. She moved her hands to rest on his wide shoulders and found herself lightly testing the warm, firm muscles under the thin fabric of his shirt.

Reason told Shelly to step back quickly. Instinct told her to go forward, to meet Dan halfway. Torn, she stood still, not giving anything, but not rejecting his mouth as it settled lightly. His lips rubbed across the softness of hers once, then again. Sugar kisses. If it was all she could ever have, she would have been content simply remembering the look of him, the warmth of his smile. Now she felt restless and greedy. Here he was, offering so much more.

And so Shelly stepped forward, feeling Dan move in his chair so that she was pressed closer than she should have been, but not close enough. With the third brush of his lips, all thought process shut down. He opened his mouth, and it was the most sumptuous banquet she'd ever been invited to attend.

She'd read of people coming together, creating instant combustion. She'd never thought to experience it for herself. She hadn't known a woman could feel blind panic and explosive, stomach-drop excitement all in the same heartbeat. At each point of contact, nerve ends fired. Always skeptical, she had heard it described as rockets blasting, dynamite igniting. Now, after twenty-eight years, she knew there was more to it than poetic rambling.

The greed was stunning. Like Shelly's, Dan's thought process shut down, too. Unlike Shelly, he did not pause to consider the wisdom of their actions.

He hadn't realized he was going to touch her until he did. She was small, but not fragile. Fragile meant easily broken, weak. She was neither. Fragile didn't pulse. It didn't explode under a man's fingertips.

Shelly Barker was a deceptive woman. Because of her wariness, the containment in her eyes, Dan expected to have to woo her closer. There was nothing distant about the woman he tugged forward to sprawl across his lap. He hadn't meant to hold her, not as if she belonged to him, yet his hand found its own way to the subtle curve of her breast. Her trembling response demanded that he touch. When he did, his own hand shook.

It wasn't enough.

Dan had promised himself only a taste. The thought came, then disappeared with the soft, hungry sounds she made in her throat. One kiss merged with another, veered, returned. His mouth may have left her lips, but not her flesh. Still working on the same taste, he rationalized, learning the shape of her ear, savoring any uncovered skin he could reach, breathing her in. She was delicious.

He made other discoveries. Shifting her slight weight on his lap, Dan discovered how delicately she was made; narrow hips and porcelain bones; lean, resilient muscles. He knew how she would feel twined around him, all bright, kinetic energy. He pulled her closer, fitting her to the contours of his own body. She made him groan and swell, made him ache for the pleasure of her hands on his. Her clothes, he decided, were a damned nuisance.

Finally, it was the loss of control that brought Dan to his senses. In a vague corner of his mind, sanity was questioned. This had gone beyond tentative the moment he had touched her. His body demanded the logical outcome. The situation was becoming that precarious.

Dan did not want to take his mouth away, but he did. He could feel Shelly's heart beating furiously under his hand, but not any faster than his own. There was still a soft, scented spot just where her neck met her shoulder that he hadn't explored. He didn't want to leave it. He had felt but not tasted the sweet, cushioned mounds of her breasts.

With reluctance, slowly, Dan withdrew. He took her hand, kissing the fingertips, the soft palm, the fragile blue veins in her wrist. There would be, he decided, a better place and time than in his aunt's house with all the family upstairs.

He felt the deep tremor in her body the moment sanity returned to Shelly. He knew by the way she stiffened against him that she wanted to leave, but he tightened his hold. The house slept as he held Shelly Barker on his lap, running his hands up and down her back, as much to soothe her as to calm himself.

The shame, Shelly decided, should be coming soon. A woman with any principles would not find herself sprawled over a man she barely knew and had no intention of getting involved with even if she did. By no stretch of the imagination would that woman stay, cocooned by silence, wishing it didn't have to end.

Waiting for remorse, the most Shelly could manage was regret.

Dan lifted the hand he'd been nuzzling and laid it against his cheek. "Lady, you pack a powerful punch." Angling his head, he tried to decipher her quiet expression. When he could not, he asked, "What are you thinking?"

Shelly spoke slowly, "I'm trying to feel guilty."

"Why?"

"Because I don't know you." Her answer was honest because she refused to hide behind anything else. She alone was responsible for her actions and the consequences of them. Coming to a decision, she pushed away from Dan and began clearing the remains of their feast from the table. At the sink, she turned back. "I've never crawled over a man before in my life. I can't decide if I should be ashamed or proud of myself."

Dan watched as she rechanneled her energy into a quick, vital animation. "If we're going to do any damning here, keep in mind that I started it." He, too, stood up and walked to the counter. "Maybe I'm the one who should be feeling guilty." Tipping his head to one side, he jumped back to her last statement. "What if I weren't such a stranger?"

Shelly nearly sighed. "I enjoyed what happened very much, but let's not get carried away here."

Dan blinked. He'd never heard those exact words come from a woman's mouth. At least not directed toward himself. His lips quirked at the corner, and he felt the faintest impulse to laugh. In his opinion, it was a bit late for caution.

"What if I called you?" he persisted. "What if we went through a normal relationship progression?"

"Couldn't we just say we both reacted oddly to the Cocoa Puffs?"

Despite himself, Dan grinned. "I don't think we can blame any of this on indigestion. Anyway, what's wrong with seeing more of each other?"

Shelly returned his smile with a smaller one. Her gaze took in the shadowy displays of crystal, silver and china in the heavy, antique cabinets. She glanced at the immaculate tiled counters, the polished hardwoods and the gleaming appliances. All was tastefully organized, beautifully decorated, whispering of old money and breeding. Everything about the room spoke of a complacent, serene life-style.

Everything her life was not or ever could be.

For a moment, Dan might believe in possibilities, but Shelly knew better. "One or two things that I can think of," she said, answering his question.

"Such as?" Dan found himself enjoying this strange conversation almost as much as he had enjoyed holding the energy of her supple body in his arms. Shelly Barker reminded him of a softly colored shaft of light, moving from place to place around the shadowy room. He could see her impatience with his questioning in the quick push of her hair away from her face, the pout of her full mouth. A mouth he planned on tasting again.

"In case no one's thought to mention it," Shelly said, gathering her argument, "you're the Prince Charming type...up here on your mountain. I live down in the real world, and in my world, I have obligations I can't change...won't change. And why would you come down?" She whirled around. "One of two reasons that I can think of. To continue where we left off—" she waved a hand sharply toward the recently vacated chair "—and you'd be going to an awful lot of trouble for sex, or..."

"Or...?" Dan prodded curiously.

"I can't think of a second reason."

"What if," he said with deceptive calm, "we left our respective turfs for neutral ground? What if I turned in my crown and you quit worrying about it? Why couldn't we take this a step at a time and see where it led us?"

"That wouldn't work." She shook her head. "Once a prince, always a prince."

"What if I want to call you, Shelly Barker?"

A slender hand came out and sliced the air with quick, impatience. "I tell you, Dan, even if we fell wildly in love with each other—" *Ha* "—it wouldn't make a damn bit of difference. I don't have time for you to call. I have a brother...I did mention my brother, didn't I?"

"I believe so," Dan said slowly, curiously. "In the same breath that I first mentioned my mother."

She didn't want to smile, but it came anyway. Then she sobered, and told him, "My brother is disabled. I am his only living relative."

Dan dropped his eyes, noticing that one of his shirt buttons had come undone. A moment went by as he fixed it. His gaze was calm, but faintly puzzled when he looked back at Shelly.

"So? I am my mother's firstborn, only male offspring. And in case you hadn't noticed, she happens to be a tyrant."

He had a point there, Shelly conceded, but he didn't understand about Richard Robert. How could he? Her sense of humor came to the rescue and, with the kitchen restored, she took a step closer to her room, back toward the shadows.

At this moment, Dan Sutherland was as caught up in the fantasy as she was. But with the return of sanity, there was as much chance of him calling her, Shelly Barker, the dressmaker, as there was of the sun shifting itself to orbit the earth. Whatever had caused his reaction, whether it be impulse, novelty or rampaging hormones, would be gone with the morning light.

Not that she would trade away these past few minutes. He had given her much to take home. She wouldn't exchange the experience for a fistful of diamonds. However, she wasn't about to repeat it. Not with Dan Sutherland.

From the dungeon door, she looked up, and the smile she gave him was tight. "I'm nearly finished altering Debra's gown," she told him. "I'll be finished tonight and gone by morning."

"I can't leave... not yet." Dan shrugged, feeling that he was missing something important. He didn't understand her smile or the reason behind it. "I have to see this wedding out. I have unfinished commitments to get back to, loose ends. You understand that, don't you, Shelly?"

She understood perfectly. No doubt when the fog cleared his brain, he would have trouble remembering her name. And if he did call, she couldn't stop him, but she could warn him.

"I live in a strange place, not always wonderful. Not easy like this." Her gaze swept through the quiet serenity of the room. "Tonight we were anything we wanted to be. Keep it here and neither one of us will be disappointed."

"If we don't?"

"There are trolls and dragons at my place, Dan. Princes don't last long."

"Shelly." Impatience roughed his voice and moved his shoulders. "I'd like to see you again."

"Why don't we try this," she suggested brightly. "You think about what I've said. In the event that you're still interested—" her hand went for the doorknob and there was the faintest trace of mischief in her smile "—feel free to call.

Or better yet, drop by when you're in town again...we'll do the royal-lunch thing."

Dan stood for a moment, staring at the spot where she'd been. He wasn't certain he understood all her coded messages, but he believed the gist of them was, if a man chose to venture into Shelly Barker's life, he'd better go prepared with a sword.

Twelve hours later, Dan once again stalked his Aunt Megan's kitchen. Pacing, swearing, he came to a halt in front of the bay window and stared out over a pristine winter landscape. Superficially, the room was unchanged, but he felt the difference. The elusive, wispy current of life and energy from last night was gone.

Dan was spoiled. If confronted, he'd be the first to admit it. His mother and sisters indulged him. Pride and wonder had puffed the father's chest from the son's first lusty wail. With his quick mind, Dan excelled in and relished the part he played in expanding the family empire. Because of his long, muscular body and almost too-pretty face, it was fair to say there had never been anything he wanted that he could not have.

He was not used to waiting in line, questioning his own motives or deliberate anarchy.

Shelly had warned that she'd be gone in the morning, but he thought she'd stay until he could get back from the wedding breakfast. He thought she'd at least stay long enough to say goodbye. Hell, if truth came to dare, he hadn't thought she'd *want* to leave without seeing him first.

Wrong. He'd come down at seven-thirty to find the suite empty. The way he figured it, Shelly had been on her way home before the sun came up.

His ego was bent double. He was tired, frustrated and just testy enough to snarl. Flexing his fingers, he inhaled through his mouth in a slow, controlled movement.

It didn't help much.

"Oh, my!" Megan came into the kitchen, sniffed, gasped and spun toward the counter. "What is that smell?"

Coffee had been left on the burner hours too long, and even though Dan had taken it off when he'd come in, the burned, bitter smell hung tenaciously in the air.

Someone had also used bug spray recently. His guess would be his mother, since she had an unreasonable vendetta against creepy crawlers. Except that his aunt would not allow such a thing entry into her house, or that most of the insect population hibernated in the dead of winter, anyway. Linda had used enough spray to annihilate half of them from the mountain. A sweet, cloying perfume had been used to mask the heavy chemical and that, mixed with the burned coffee, could produce a knee-jerk reaction in the unprepared.

Dan took a stool at the breakfast counter and continued to breathe carefully through his mouth.

Megan whirled around. "I *know* I hid the bug bomber. Damn, damn! How on earth does she find it?" She coughed. "No, don't answer me. She is your mother. I'm going to make a fresh pot of coffee—no, tea—and then I'm going up to my bedroom and lock myself in. If anyone should ask, you haven't seen me, you don't know me." Stopping midchatter, she walked to the breakfast counter, reached across and touched his arm. "What is it, Danny? Is all this wedding fun getting to you, too?"

Dan gave his aunt a long, thoughtful look. "No, nothing like that. I need information," he told her, "and at this stage of the game, I feel like a total ass for having to ask."

"Dan?"

"I want to hear about Shelly Barker. She's gone, by the way, did you know?"

For a moment, Megan looked blank. "Oh, yes, Debra did say she tried the gown on this morning, early. She was not too pleased about that. It fit beautifully—the gown, that is. Shelly said she'd be in touch about her bill."

A thoughtful frown replaced the chatter. She appeared to be racking her mental resources, searching for a plausible reason why her favorite nephew would want information about the woman who had designed his cousin's wedding gown. Then, tentatively, she asked, "Are you thinking of having a dress made for someone?"

Dan had to laugh. "Try again." His voice changed, became harshly controlled. "Is she married?"

Megan jerked back in startled bewilderment. "No...I don't think so. She told me she lives alone. What is this all about?"

To avoid her question for a moment, Dan asked one of his own. "What do you know about Shelly?"

"Not a great deal?" Megan murmured, thinking hard. "A friend of Debra's recommended her to us. I know she's in demand, because it was next to impossible to get an appointment. Evidently the Sutherland name didn't impress her enough to come running. Of course, the harder it was to pin Shelly down, the more obstinate Debra became. She finally did come up here with her portfolio. As soon as her book was open, we knew Shelly had to be the one to design Debra's gown."

Dan listened with focused intensity. "That's it? You must have had time and contact with her when she first made the dress, and then she was here for two days. That's all you know?"

"I'm thinking." Megan waved a shushing hand. "It's not as if she owed us a personal history." She tapped her chin thoughtfully before continuing. "Reserved... that's my impression. When Shelly came up those few times for fittings, and while she was here just now, she spent a lot of time listening and watching, but I can't remember her volunteering much more information about herself than what I've told you. Yesterday she just seemed to *be* here—now she's gone. I hate to admit this, but I don't believe anyone really noticed Shelly while she was here."

No, Dan thought, that wasn't accurate. Someone had noticed.

"She liked your Uncle Rolf. I remember she had the sweetest little laugh for one of his atrocious jokes. But yesterday, when my boys were around, she seemed to disappear. That's odd... isn't that odd?"

"Not all women make fools of themselves over your dynamic duo, Meggie."

"You're included, and you darn well know it. Women have been making asses of themselves over you three for the last fifteen years."

Dan grinned at her. "I think it's the name and the family bank account."

"Not in Shelly's case. She didn't make a scene with any of you boys, and she certainly had the opportunity. Remember the little blond friend Debra brought home from school the last summer you stayed with us?" Megan said with a faint laugh. "Grief, the way that little hussy came swishing down every morning in those nighties, she might as well have stuck a sign on her chest to advertise."

"She did. It's just that none of us were buying."

"Wait a minute! You drove up with Shelly. Why are you asking me these questions? I can't believe a young woman wouldn't tell you anything you wanted to know."

"My name and pretty face didn't seem to work for me this time, Meggie," Dan admitted, his voice tinged with self-mockery. Swiveling around on the stool, he stretched his long legs out toward the bay window. "Not with Ms. Barker."

Megan's mouth dropped open. "Are you telling me there's a personal reason behind these questions? Personal...as in you and Shelly Barker?"

Dan shot her a teasing grin. "I told you I didn't want a new dress."

"Oh, my." Running distracted fingers through her short, dark curls, Megan walked to the refrigerator. In the top freezer compartment she unearthed two fudge pops from a stash she kept hidden behind the ice-maker. "Oh, my." She offered one to Dan.

Dan peeled the wrapper down to the stick. Some men had relatives who baked cookies. Megan hid Fudgesicles and Pop-Tarts. He took a sharp bite out of the frozen confection, shot his aunt a short, level look, chewed and swallowed. "I haven't figured out what the problem is, but the lady's predawn sprint down the mountain is a clue. In essence, I believe she was telling me to take a hike."

Megan went quiet. Then she said, "How could Shelly Barker *not* like you?"

"I wouldn't say that, exactly," he murmured, remembering last night. Shelly with her guard down, soft and shaken. For a few stolen minutes, she had emphatically *liked* him. Her *liking* had scorched them both with its white-hot heat. He knew he hadn't been the only one scalded in this very room.

Her abrupt departure had the power to infuriate Dan. He controlled the surge of anger, but the simmer of it moved through his veins; the adrenaline pumped, and his gut tightened. During the hours since he'd found Shelly gone, he'd learned to live with a number of foreign emotions.

"What happened? Between you two?"

"Nothing..." *Everything,* "Yet..." He continued with a biting smile. "She forgot to give me a private number or address. That's what I need from you."

Megan hesitated. "Well, yes, I have her address. But, Dan, what are you going to do?"

"Why, Meggie," Dan drawled, "that's easy."

Shrugging his wide shoulders, he surged to his feet and stalked again to the window. Since Ms. Barker hadn't seen fit to say goodbye, her parting remark gave him his next cue. Despite the fact that Shelly's invitation had been one of those meaningless, let's-get-together routines, his plan was to take her up on the offer.

His grin as he turned back to his aunt was a shade short of nasty. "Next time I'm free and in town, I'm going to drop by."

## *Chapter Five*

Finally Friday—a vile, miserable, frustrating Friday, to be sure—two weeks, six days and eleven hours after the wedding. Dan's day had started before 5:00 a.m. with a flight out of Tampa. He'd spent the better part of the morning in Cincinnati waiting for snow plows to clear the runway so that he could reach Salt Lake City where three inches of new snow covered the ground.

At the rental-car counter, he'd spend another forty-five minutes fuming while a young clerk wiped out the company's computer system with Dan's own, never-wait, preferred customer, platinum card. Once he managed to obtain a vehicle and leave the airport, he was immediately ensnarled in the treacherous winter traffic.

At 5:00 p.m., he found himself at the north end of the artery inching his way south... along with ten or twenty thousand other crazed, impatient commuters. He shook a fist at an elderly, lilac-haired woman in the '68 Camaro when she shot in from the left, then slowed way down. Smothering a laugh, his first for the day, he rolled his shoulders to ease the kinks. The sweet little driver of the big, bad muscle car made an obscene gesture.

With the laughter, pressure eased in his chest. Dan wasn't used to the anger he'd been feeling lately. Because he could not control the situation he found himself in, frustration continually simmered beneath his surface calm. Rationally, he knew the irrationality of his own behavior. In the past three weeks, he'd done nothing but snarl. It wasn't like him to go one on one with bespeckled, lavender-tinted grannies. The problem was, he felt anything but rational.

He, Dan Sutherland, had crossed the line between desiring a thing and being obsessed by it.

His mind was made up. He didn't understand all that was pushing him toward Shelly Barker. Anger, yes, a deep abiding fury he couldn't explain, could not bank. Ego came into it. Outraged male pride. Conceit. Frustration. All of the above. None of the above.

Whatever was pushing him, it was going to take more than a few inches of snow and a little traffic to shake him. Dan was determined to surprise one skinny little redhead, even if he had to get to her sliding sideways.

Which was, sporadically, what he had to do. In giving directions, his aunt had mentioned Shelly's "little" hill. She had not mentioned that Shelly Barker lived in the southernmost suburb of the Salt Lake Valley, halfway up the side of a vertical cliff.

The back of the rental car slid to the left. Dan set his jaw, working both wheel and pedal to come out of the skid. With the sunset had come a drop in temperature, below zero, colder. The snow had increased from crystalline flakes to howling flurries reflected in the headlights, swirling around the overhead street lamps like tossed glitter. The road was a slick of thick, heavy snow over black ice.

Only a lunatic with a death wish would be out on these roads after dark.

He drove past Shelly's street. When he realized what he'd done, he cursed and put the car in reverse to back carefully down the few yards to the intersection.

If he had thought about it at all, which he had not, Dan would have put Shelly in a trendy, renovated apartment in the Avenue District. He could even picture her settled in one of those town house villages with flower boxes under each of the windows. His mistake was in assuming Shelly Barker would live somewhere normal.

Dan had not envisioned her living at the end of a dead-end road, halfway up the side of a mountain. He never would have put her in a house set so far back in the trees, the only way he could tell there was a house was from the mailbox at the top of the driveway. He would have given her neighbors. He would have given her paved roads. Hell, if he could have, he would have given her a snowplow.

He would not have given her a sudden bank of bare aspen trees marking the abrupt end of the road or a ditch two feet from her driveway.

Instinctively, Dan slammed on the brake pedal and began sliding... sideways, a little to the right and down. The heavy car came to a slow, dignified stop—or as dignified a stop as a Lincoln could make with its right rear tire ten inches lower than its left.

Dan wondered if spinning his wheels would get him out of the ditch, then decided swearing would be just as effective. He did both.

Having stopped work for a moment, Shelly was in the process of heating water for tea when she heard the unique whine of tires spinning against ice. It was quiet this far up, and a still, cold night had a way of amplifying sound.

Since the only streetlight was at the top of the road, Shelly tried mashing her nose against the front window for a better view. A car, headlights on, continued to dig trenches in the snow with its tires. She was surprised to see icy flakes pelt down when not a few minutes before there had been none. These were the kind of blanketing, biting white flurries that had been falling off and on since Thanksgiving.

People occasionally turned off on her road by mistake. Sometimes, when it snowed like this, the dead-end sign got covered over. If the car was as close to the driveway as it looked, the car's occupants would be needing more help than a push. That ditch was a killer.

Shelly dashed to the hall closet. Pulling out her ski parka, she shoved a heavy knit cap over her ears and remembered to grab a pair of gloves.

Outside was numbing cold, and the blowing wind stung. She slid across the iced over welcome mat on the porch and jumped down the front steps to sink thigh deep into unshoveled snow. Since walking would be difficult no matter which way she went, she left the sidewalk to cut diagonally across the lawn.

As she got closer to the car, shapes began to take form through the whirling storm. Her initial assessment was right on the money. The car was stuck where she thought it would be, the worst place it could be. In the ditch.

Next to the car, a huge gray shape of a man turned the frigid air bluer with wonderfully descriptive language...and he viciously kicked the wheel of a fine piece of technology.

Shelly was brave, to a point, and she stepped closer.

"You know," she began conversationally, raising her voice to a muffled roar, "you're in danger of damaging a rim."

The cursing stopped. The shape turned, almost comically startled, just as if it hadn't heard a grown woman thrashing and panting her way through thirty yards of waist-high snow.

"What the hell is a damned ditch doing here, anyway?"

Shelly couldn't help but smile. The wind took half his words, but his attitude was explicit. It always amused her to see an adult male throw a temper tantrum, and this one was more entertaining than most. His hat was pulled low over his ears, the collar of his great coat up around them. The only thing she could see was a glitter in his eyes as he swung around. The muffled sound of his growl was thoroughly tantalizing, horribly fed up and indignantly offended.

Of course, he would be. Anyone with an ounce of sense would have known better than to come ice-skating up the side of her hill on a night like this. But this man had the amazing ability to make it sound as if his situation was all her fault...and that she would be dealt with accordingly. A woman couldn't help but admire his technique.

"Why isn't this road plowed?" the shape growled again, circling the Lincoln and shaking his head as if he still couldn't understand how *his* car had gotten stuck in *her* ditch.

Was it her imagination, or was this man a tad overbearing? A touch obnoxious? Although Shelly considered herself a fair woman, her smile tilted. She let out a long breath.

"I'll speak to the Highway Department first thing in the morning." She thought it best to humor him. Stepping gingerly up to the car, she bent down, squinting through the snow to assess the damage. Nothing looked broken, just stuck. "Meanwhile, if you need help—and you do—I'm it. Do you belong to an auto club?"

"Yes," he hissed, "I belong to the auto club." The snow was getting heavier, thicker, coming faster. She had to shout to be heard. He couldn't seem to do much more than sulk.

This hulk certainly wasn't going to win any points for charm. Shelly took a cautious step back. Yanking her woolly cap farther down over her ears, she tried again. "Would you like to use my phone?"

"I hate it when women humor me," Dan mumbled, breathing hard to control his frustration. Pulling the collar of his coat up higher over his neck and ears, he kicked the tire again. This was not the scenario he had planned. Instead of catching Shelly at a disadvantage, he was the one stuck on a mountain in the middle of a blizzard. No man enjoyed looking like an idiot in front of a woman, even if he was one.

Shelly suddenly decided enough was enough. Her nose was beginning to run, and she didn't have a tissue. She hadn't taken the time to change into boots. And sneakers, she decided, had not been the wisest of choices. The hulk could kick his tire until it fell off, it wasn't going to get him out of the ditch. "You're welcome to use my phone," she offered again as she turned back to the house.

The kettle was whistling, its pitch high and shrill, as she entered the kitchen through the door off the carport. Shedding coat, gloves and hat, she switched it off before heading to the bedroom. Snow clung to her pants, had crept past her socks into her sneakers and was melting around her ankles. From the belt loops of her jeans down, she was soggy wet and freezing.

The jeans were quickly replaced with thick, brown corduroy trousers, and the shoes for a pair of men's insulated wool socks. They were the gray kind with the red heel and toe that fit when she had boots on, but that had a tendency to slide down her ankles when she wore them alone.

"Got a spare towel?"

Although she had left the side door ajar, she hadn't realized the hulk had followed her in. She moved from the bedroom to the linen closet, then she hurried into the kitchen. "I didn't—" The towel in her hand fell from her fingers. Shelly's eyes widened, and her jaw sagged.

"I was sure my big entrance lost its punch in the ditch out there." Dan's smile was acid as he walked in front of her and bent down to pick up the towel. "But maybe not." Unwanted humor lit his narrowed gaze as, with a fingertip under her chin, he closed her mouth. "Since I'm in town and since I have a little free time, I thought we'd do lunch. Surprise!"

The energy of the storm had come in with him. Shelly thought that if she turned off the lights, she would be able to see static sparks crackling. Dan's face was stiff from the cold, but she wasn't fooled by the tight stretching of his lips across his perfect white teeth. His grin wasn't frozen, it was pure nasty.

"I thought you were in Tampa." With trembling fingers, she searched for the nearest something to hold on to.

"I was in Tampa. Everything is intact," he said in a soft, mildly amused voice. "The family empire continues to expand and flourish. The other cousins are pleased to have a certain land contract tucked neatly away in the family vault." He took a moment to run the towel over his damp hair. He out of all the cousins could be counted on for his calm, matter-of-fact control. He was the quiet one, the pragmatic thinker. He was known to weigh every angle of a situation before giving an opinion or taking action. Logic before emotion.

Not this time.

"Four calls, Shelly? An invitation to Tampa...no strings attached. How many messages did I leave on your answering machine?"

She should have seen this coming, she thought, and before her knees gave out, she groped her way to the table. She really should have expected this, she decided, sinking into the handiest chair. Hadn't Spencer been the same way? Tenacious, determined to have his way in all things, adamant when it came to speaking the final word.

Why hadn't she guessed there would be similarities between the two men? Both came from privileged backgrounds, both were successful, spoiled and more charming than they had a right to be. If she had thought it through more carefully, she would have been expecting Dan Sutherland on her doorstep. She'd have known that ignoring him was the worst possible method of handling such a man.

Dan's rampage up her hill ran so true to type, she nearly smiled. Apparently, there was a subspecies of male that thrived on challenge. The less subtle the "no, thank you," the more determined they became.

Shelly wanted to throw up her hands. No matter what she should have done or known, she wasn't prepared for this. For the first time since he'd walked out on her, she was glad she'd known Spencer Smith. The experience had left her wiser. Without it, she would not have felt confident enough to deal with the frustrated male stalking the perimeters of her kitchen, dripping melting snow as he went.

It seemed like hours since he'd spoken. Actually, less than a minute had past. Shelly cleared her throat and dredged up a smile. She could only hope she didn't look as intimidated as she felt.

"Hello, Dan. I'm surprised to see you." Her remark lacked flair, didn't begin to encompass the enormity of the situation, but was the best she could do.

Since she didn't appear as if she was going to offer to do it, Dan hung his own coat on a peg by the door. He was feeling a little smug and a lot satisfied. Shelly Barker was doing her best to gather her composure, and to an extent, she was succeeding. What she couldn't do was take back her initial shocked reaction or hide the quick, frantic pulse pounding at the base of her white throat.

Walking to the sink, he rummaged for a glass in the overhead cabinet and ran himself some water. He could afford to take events slow and easy now. He had her cornered.

Turning, Dan leaned a hip against the sink and gave her a slow, deliberate smile. "You didn't expect to see me at all, did you, Shelly?"

There was a quality to his smile that wasn't doing a thing for her nerves. Striving for calm that kept threatening to slip, she lifted her chin and kept her eyes on his. "No," she admitted in an admirably steady voice, "I didn't."

"I told you I'd be in touch after my business was cleared away."

She shook her head. "You didn't say you would. You threw out a general question...something about, what would happen if you did?"

"But it wasn't a general question. It was pretty damned specific. I did call."

Shelly's eyes skittered away from his. She began an intense examination of her left thumbnail. "I know," she muttered.

Dan cocked his head. "What?"

Her shoulders rose and fell. She glanced at him, then away. "I know," she said again, louder.

"I left messages on your machine. Are you going to tell me you were too busy to answer any of them?"

The shock was wearing off and her courage was returning. Who was this man to land in her ditch without an invitation and then imperiously demand explanations? She wished she'd mastered the art of the haughty glare, but the best she had ever been able to do was a squint-eyed sort of pout. Besides, she thought she'd try the rational approach first.

"I stopped answering after the first few times we talked because I assumed that if I did, you'd give up and go away. I didn't think you were serious."

Dan was quiet for a moment. "All those calls... an invitation to Florida," he said finally in a patient, gentle voice, "and you didn't think I was serious? If nothing else, the fact that I'm here, Shelly, should give you a clue."

The sarcasm made her hesitate, but she answered calmly. "You're here because you're angry." She nodded slowly, gathering the courage to continue. "I'll bet your black book is the size of the Yellow Pages. Women just jump when you call. My guess is, this has never happened to you before. Ego, that's why you're here. You have to tell me off... it's a matter of honor." She nodded again, as if coming to a decision. "Okay, we can do it your way."

Smiling faintly, she clasped her hands together on the table. "Do you want something to warm you up before you get aggressive? A drink, some soup?"

Her deductive reasoning hit the bull's eye, but not dead center. Yes, all of those things had driven Dan up her mountain. There was, however, more to it than that. He could have told her that after the third unanswered message, he'd decided to forget the whole business. But if he went that far, he'd have to go on to admit that since the night in his aunt's kitchen, Shelly had never left his thoughts. He wondered if the word *obsession* would unsettle her as much as it did him.

Watching her, seated so primly and expectantly at the table, Dan felt the urge to laugh. She wore a green-checked shirt tonight. Not flannel, but some heavy material that swamped her from collarbone to thigh. Underneath the shirt was another one, and the cuffs of her baggy brown pants looked to have been rolled up at least twice. He had to wonder about those socks. Either those tiny feet of hers were still cold, or she didn't realize how hard she was rubbing the one on top of the other. Whatever the reason, she was about to lose the left sock. The end of it was about eight inches shy of her toe and sliding fast.

Shelly Barker was not showing the proper amount of respect. She was also right in assuming situations like this occurred rarely, if ever. In the normal course of events, when a Sutherland growled, everyone ducked. Hell! She knew he was a rich man. He was also a damned busy one, and, yes, he *had* been practicing his tirade. He'd meant to blast her with it the minute he walked through the door.

Dan let out a long breath and moved his shoulders to ease the knotted muscles in his neck and back. It had been one hell of a drive. His eyes burned, he hadn't eaten in over eight hours, and his teeth were swimming from the coffee he'd had earlier.

How was a man supposed to rage at a woman who couldn't even keep her socks on?

"Yeah," he said at last, "I'd like some." At her blank look, he shrugged. "A hot drink and soup... a whole can, if you've got it. And what about indoor plumbing? Have you got your own this far up, or do I go outside?"

"Oh." Flustered, Shelly waved her hand. "It's through the living room to the hall on the right, first door."

When Dan finished cleaning up, he hesitated in the narrow hall instead of going right back to the kitchen. This was Shelly's home, these were her things. Nothing here was his concern. It was a case of snooping, pure and simple, but he needed answers to still the nagging question in his mind. And if she had secrets, she'd left the doors wide open.

What was it about Shelly Barker that drove him on? And after banging his head against her wall, why the hell didn't she let him in?

The room directly across the hall must have been a bedroom and was now used as a work-and-storage area. Shelves lined the main inner wall and were stacked with bolts of fabric and plastic containers. Two sewing machines, one of them odd looking, sat on a large worktable along with at least half a dozen cones of threads. By the look of it, she had been working.

In a corner, tacked on the wall, were several long butcher-paper sheets of sketches. Dan didn't know much about dress designing, but if the pieces of ivory-colored material pinned onto the mannequin eventually resembled the sketches on the wall, Shelly's creation would be more than a gown; it would be a work of art.

He went to stand at the threshold of the second door down the hall. His interest sharpened. The bed was one of those narrow, twin-size affairs only a child could sleep in. No, he decided, shaking his head. That assumption wasn't totally accurate. A woman Shelly's size could sleep in that bed. Somehow, though, he didn't see her comfortable in a room wallpapered with spaceships. Nor could he picture her completing the half-finished Lego sculpture on the desk or shooting the Nerf ball into the plastic hoop attached to the back side of the door.

So, Dan continued the thought logically, if the room belonged to a child, where was it? Since nothing in the hall gave him an answer, he left his exploration to go back to the kitchen and the woman who could furnish one.

His stomach protested as he entered. The smell alone was enough to make a strong man beg, but for the moment he was determined to ignore the growling in his belly.

"Why didn't you tell me you have a child?"

Shelly, unaware, let go of the ladle in her hand and took an instinctive step back. For the first time since he'd landed himself on her hill, she heard genuine anger in Dan's voice. As she turned to face him, her eyes were wide and wary.

"What are you talking about? I don't have any children."

"You don't have to lie to me, Shelly."

"Lie?" she repeated in confusion. "Why should I?"

Dan cut her off with an impatient sweep of his hand. "I saw his room, his toys. Where is he?"

Shelly closed her eyes and took a deep, calming breath. When she opened them again, her gaze was calm and direct. "The only toys in this house belong to my brother...I'm sure I told you about him. Those are his things. He doesn't live with me anymore, but he stays often." She took another breath. "Now I've got a question for you."

Before she asked it, Shelly finished ladling out a deep dish of the barley soup she'd made earlier that day. From the oven, she retrieved slices of homemade French bread that had been toasted to a warm, golden brown. On the table, cocoa sat cooling in a tall, ceramic mug.

Shelly waited until Dan seated himself. Now wasn't the time for temper. Not even if her blood was beginning to boil with it. Spencer had told her time and again that she lacked self-control. He'd often accused her of laughing too hard, crying too much or getting upset too easily. Well, not this time. This time what she meant to be was calm and logical.

Standing away from the table, she crossed her arms over her chest. "Who gave you the right to snoop around my home...poke into my privacy like a damned Peeping Tom?"

Of course, she was right. What he'd done was out of line, and he knew it. Dan took a spoonful of the soup, savoring it thoroughly in the few seconds he figured he had left before she let loose and blasted him back out into the cold.

"I was looking for your reason," he explained, then took another hasty bite.

"What?"

And he wasn't, he decided, about to get thrown out before he tasted the bread. The last time he'd eaten homemade bread was... He couldn't remember the last time. Meanwhile, watching Shelly grittily hold on to her temper was nothing if not enlightening.

"I said," he repeated patiently, "that I was looking for your reason. I wanted to know why you left my aunt's house without saying goodbye to me. I was curious to know why you ignored each and every one of the calls I left on your answering machine. When I found the toys, I thought I'd found something to go on."

Dumbfounded, Shelly could only shake her head. "Do you realize how arrogant you sound? You Sutherlands are an incredible family. What were you going to do if I had a child?" Her voice was raising in volume and pitch, and she made a concentrated effort to calm down. "What possible difference would one make?"

Dan shrugged easily. "None that I could see...unless there was also a husband around that you hadn't bothered to tell me about. Having one of those lurking in the background would explain your silence. For a minute I thought you cheated."

Shelly's thought process took a temporary leave of absence. Men were fascinating creatures. Especially the rare kind that assumed they owned the world. Things like this did not happen with ordinary men.

She walked to the window, staring out at the stark winter scene as she gathered her thoughts. Just since his arrival, an inch of snow had fallen. She wondered how much more there would be before morning. He'd have to stay the night. She knew how treacherous the drive up her hill must have been. Going down, under these conditions, would be sheer stupidity...assuming they could get his car out of the ditch.

"What made you decide to live on the side of a mountain?"

The whimsy in his quiet question brought a smile to her own voice. "In the first place, we locals don't consider this a mountain. It's a hill, on a bit of an incline. And I live here because...it's my home. My father built this place for my brother and me. Dad worked at the copper mine, double shifts for years, so that we could have a house high above the valley. I promised him that I would always keep it as a family home."

Remembering the rest of the promises she'd made to her father brought Shelly around. With a bright, determined smile, she left the window and took a seat across the table from her guest. Time for plain speaking.

"When you came up here, Dan, what was it you expected?"

To avoid the candor he saw in her light eyes, Dan gathered the remains of his meal from the table and walked to the sink. For a moment their positions were reversed, Dan looking out through the window, Shelly in a chair at the table.

"What do you suppose," he asked absently as he watched the snow, "my chances are of getting down the hill tonight?"

Shelly wished for both their sakes that she had another answer to give him. "None," she told him honestly. "You might want to call the auto club to get your name on the waiting list for tomorrow morning, but nothing comes up here when it snows like this." The original question was in her voice as she persisted. "Dan?"

He inhaled slowly and turned to face her. "Would you believe that I didn't think past getting here?"

Her features softened with an unruly smile as humor lit her eyes. "I'd believe you weren't thinking." Her smile turned to laughter, and she stood up. "And they say women are the illogical sex! Dan, I never believed you'd take what happened in your aunt's kitchen this far. There isn't one logical reason for you to be here, but one hundred and one why you shouldn't."

Swinging around, she threw her arms wide, keeping them open so that nothing about her person was hidden from him. "We, you and I, make no sense at all. Take the very least of it." She laughed again. "I'm only as tall as your breastbone. Have you thought about what bending down on a consistent basis can do to a man's back? And while we're on the subject, I haven't any, breasts that is. I wear layers of clothes because that's the only way I look...more. I have orange hair and freckles. I'm not the kind of woman men lust over."

She turned another laughing circle and pointed her finger, accusing, "You are physically perfect. In fact, that smile of yours should come with a warning label. If what you expected was sex, you went to an awful lot of trouble. No doubt you can have it anytime, anywhere you want."

"Shelly," Dan chided gently, "it's not done that way anymore."

She would have agreed with him, but she was on a roll and refused to be sidetracked. "Your family can trace its history back to the settlement of this valley. They don't belong to the social elite, they *started* it. My father was a miner at the copper pit. My mother packed her suitcase and left after my brother was born. I'm a dressmaker, for pity's sake. I have no redeeming social value."

"I don't remember asking for a pedigree."

Shelly whirled around the kitchen. Her humor had played itself out. Frustration took its place. "Those are just the superficial reasons why I didn't meet you in Tampa or answer any of your damned messages. Let's get down to some real differences."

Ah, Dan thought, now it comes. She was moving around the room with a suppressed volatility, never stopping as she paced. He had to wonder if she was a thrower—plates, glasses, that kind of thing.

She might be, he decided a moment later, if she ever let go of that self-control she tried so hard to maintain. He'd bet she had a great arm. She was captivating and fascinating...and what she was saying made no damned sense at all. "What? Say that again . . . slower this time."

Shelly took a deep breath and repeated patiently, "I'm trying to point out how different our life-styles are, and I was using the microwave as an example. Specifically, my lack of one. You, no doubt, take things like that for granted, while I couldn't even consider having one around. Don't you see? You live in Denver, but think nothing of packing up and flying off. You belong to a world that puts you anywhere, anytime. I rarely leave this valley. Those dragons and trolls I was telling you about are packaged right into my life."

Maybe it was because she made absolutely no sense. Maybe he was just plain tired. Or maybe, he decided, it was because he'd been in her home for over an hour and she was still trying to kick him out. Whatever it was that struck the spark to his temper, Dan had suddenly had enough. This was, all things considered, one hell of a first date.

"Shelly." His voice was a quiet, gritty rumble. "Perhaps by my coming here I did presume too much." Okay, he thought, he could admit it. "But it's time you slowed down and took a breath.'' He still didn't understand what a microwave had to do with anything, but he was willing to give her the point. ''It's not as if I've asked you to marry me.''

He was right. Humiliation came to Shelly first, a swift, hot tide followed by a sudden, ridiculous hurt. Here she was rambling on and on about the impossibility of a lifetime commitment, and he'd done nothing but show up on her doorstep.

With quiet dignity, Shelly lifted her head and looked straight at him. ''No,'' she said slowly, ''you didn't. I have a tendency to get carried away.'' Her mouth quirked in a painful attempt at humor. ''My mistake.''

Dan couldn't let it go at that. His curiosity wouldn't let it go. ''Why do you insist on making this difficult?''

Shelly's chin inched up to a set angle. ''Whatever you might say, you didn't come here to be my buddy. . . and like I said, I have a tendency to get carried away. Before you know it, I'd get used to having you around, and that would make you nervous. There isn't a snowball's chance in hell that you'd stay, and when you left, my heart would break. I don't want you here, Dan.''

## *Chapter Six*

Dan tensed as another night noise intruded in the stillness. The house settled deeper into the December storm. He rolled over again, punching the pillow that smelled of citrus and Shelly Barker. The last thing he'd wanted to do was sleep in her room, but as she had pointed out, she would fit better in her brother's narrow bed.

By rights, exhaustion should have taken his body hours ago, but his mind refused to shut down and let sleep take over. Fragmented pieces of the evening drifted in and out of his brain, a certain expression, the words she'd spoken. Anger was never far away, and neither was regret.

Dan regretted the pain he'd seen in Shelly's eyes. Though his motives for coming were vague, even suspect, he had not come to hurt her. And after what she said, he should have been eager to end this farce and get the hell off her mountain. She was right, he told himself. He was a fool for having taken this so far. The entire incident should have ended that night in his aunt's house.

Some nagging, nebulous feeling returned again and again. Along the line, he'd missed something. Evidently he hadn't been watching closely enough or he'd been too caught up in his own reaction to honestly hear what she had said. With the feeling came intangible thoughts. They refused him sleep, denied him ease. What was it, behind the stubbornness, that he'd seen in Shelly Barker's eyes?

Dan exhaled impatiently, his growl of frustration sounding overly loud in the darkness. Thrashing about in her bed wasn't the answer. Throwing back the covers, he planted his bare feet on the cold floor and reached for his discarded pants. He'd never been a fan of warm milk, but at this point, he was willing to give it a try.

He almost didn't see her. She sat perched on the countertop near the sink, her bare legs and tiny pink toes dangling in midair. A cabinet door hung open behind her head and, at his approach, she clutched something in her hand.

Dan bit back a smile as he walked silently to the refrigerator. He wouldn't swear to it, but he was almost sure he'd caught her in some forbidden act. It took a minute to find a pan and pour the milk into it. After he set it to heat, he was free to give her his full attention. He certainly had hers. She hadn't taken her wide eyes off him.

"What are you doing?"

In a purely nervous gesture, Shelly shook her hair back from her shoulders. "I'm pondering."

"What, exactly, are you pondering?"

"Oh, you know—" she cleared her throat "—the mysteries of life. Its odd little twists and turns."

"I do know." Dan nodded solemnly. "Is what you've got in your hand helping any?"

Shelly looked at her closed fingers as if she were only just aware of their existence. She looked at Dan. Slowly the fist unfurled. She gave a slight wince at the stain smearing her palm. Her ensuing offer was exquisitely polite. "It's a liqueur-filled, chocolate-covered cordial. I ponder much better when I eat them. Would you like one?"

"Are they more effective than warm milk?"

"No contest," she said instantly. Twisting, she reached up behind her to pull down a small, foil-wrapped box from the cupboard. Extending it toward him, she inched over at the same time. "Would you like to sit down?"

Dan considered her offer. The counter looked sturdy enough for her ninety-odd pounds, but since his weight was easily twice that, he decided to keep his feet planted firmly on the floor. As he dipped into her box of chocolates, he said, "After midnight, again. What would happen to us, do you suppose, if we moved this nonrelationship out of a dark kitchen?"

His eyes were well adjusted to the dimness of the room, and he could see the faint smile that came and went on her mouth.

"I think," she said slowly, "we'd both see things we didn't expect... couldn't deal with."

"Maybe we'd be surprised. Maybe we'd like what we saw."

"What if—" She hesitated, then continued in a whisper, "What if one of us decided he couldn't handle the surprises he discovered?"

Dan moved closer without being aware that he did so. "Then... we'd know."

"But by that time... the other might be... attached. Wouldn't it be safer if we just left it alone?"

"It probably would," he agreed, and found himself reaching out because his hand had memory and will of its own. This was what had driven him, the deep terrible need to touch her again.

No silk and lace for Shelly Barker. She'd have to stand up for him to be positive, but if he wasn't mistaken, her nighttime attire consisted of cotton boxer shorts and a short-sleeved undershirt. Glamorous, no, but effective. The smell of her hair gave him pleasure, the bird bones of her shoulder, the soft catch of her breath as his hand found its way under the tumble of hair.

Shelly could not seem to catch her breath. The warmth of his dark eyes left her in no doubt as to where his thoughts had gone. The same place hers were wandering. She wanted to swear, and she did, a mild little epithet that brought a chuckle from the chest of the man who touched her so gently.

"I don't want you to do this." She kept her eyes on his face, her body motionless under his hand, but the pulse in her throat was wild and rapid. "I don't want to get attached to you."

"I'm as unsure as you are, Shelly." While a whimsical smile tilted his mouth, no humor brightened the dark intensity of his eyes. "But the time to play it safe is long gone. I think it was too late back with the Cocoa Puffs."

His hand remained under her hair as he waited. He didn't expect her to be fearless, to be any more certain of what lay ahead than he, but she had to be willing to try. He refused to take or coerce.

Unable to help herself, Shelly let her gaze drop to the hard curve of his mouth. Since his arrival, she had been careful to keep a physical distance between them. Now, when the choice was hers, she chose to close that distance, leaning in to his touch, feeling a moan rise in her throat.

She groaned it away. Words were unnecessary. He wanted. She understood and accommodated by opening her legs so that he could move to stand between them. She waited, aching.

He bent. "Put your arms around me, Shelly."

She stretched, wanting, but unable to meet him halfway. "I can't touch you," she whispered. "I have chocolate on my hands."

"Where?" He took her small hand and, with his tongue, slowly began to lick each finger clean, his eyes never leaving hers.

Shelly's heart beat so fast in her chest, she thought it might burst through. With each lick of his tongue, nerve ends tightened. With each draw of his mouth, heat pooled and centered where she ached to be filled. She started to say something, but forgot what it was. A whimper escaped to take its place.

When he was done with her fingers, Dan gave her a long, slow smile. "All clean." Then he drew her hand again to his lips to kiss the tender palm. His voice was rough and slightly unsteady as he asked, "Now?"

His mouth was open, waiting, when she got there.

Their lips slanted, merged as she wrapped her arms around his neck. Her knees were at his hips, and then his hands were at her bottom, pulling her up closer, as close as he could without lifting her entirely from the counter. One kiss absorbed another, hungry mouths veered as they tasted, tested soft flesh and sensitive pulse points. Hands brushed in passing. They moved and probed, rediscovered half-remembered places, found new ones. She sighed in light, helpless pants. He whispered dark, hungry words.

Shelly became aware of it first. For just a moment she ignored it, consigned it to hell with the outside world. But like the world outside the dark kitchen, it wouldn't go away and she couldn't make it go by wishing it so. Gasping, she pulled her mouth free.

"Your pan's on fire."

Startled, Dan shuddered with a helpless laugh. "Damn right my pants are on fire."

Shelly's head dropped to his warm, hair-roughened chest. His skin was faintly damp under her cheek. "I said," she repeated weakly, "your *pan* is on fire."

Dan blinked, staring at his shaking hand as he forced it to reach over for the knob. It amazed him that he'd noticed nothing. The pan was molten hot, glowing red, the milk long since boiled away. Grabbing the closest thing at hand, the lid from Shelly's foil box, he used it to nudge the pan off the burner and into the sink.

"That's one way of getting you out of the kitchen." His laugh was short and frustrated. The smell of burned milk filled the room. "Burn it down."

"Next time—" she sighed and coughed "—just try asking."

Next time, he thought as he came back to her and rested his chin lightly on top of her head, he just might. But he would leave it until then. For now, the moment was over. He didn't need the light on to know she'd withdrawn. "You're shaking," he whispered roughly.

"I know," she murmured, holding on even when she knew she should let go. "So are you."

"Are you going to avoid this, Shelly? Pretend it didn't happen? Wish it away as a mistake two people made in the dark?"

"No." Her voice was a small, ragged sound. "I can't." She pushed weakly against his chest so that she could look up at him. "What would you consider to be the next step in a normal relationship progression?"

Dan tipped his head to one side while he considered her question. "We could spend some time together. If that works, we can negotiate from there."

Shelly was through arguing. Now the only thing left to do was *show* him how incompatible they would be. "What were your plans for tomorrow and Sunday?"

"Like I told you—" Dan shrugged "—I hadn't thought past getting here. I didn't make plans farther ahead than that."

"Then stay," she said. "Spend the weekend. I promise you an unforgettable experience."

Chasing sleep long into the night, Shelly awoke with a sudden spurt of adrenaline. She was late!

It was her own fault.

Last night she had thought seriously about following Dan Sutherland back into the main bedroom. The thing was, while she had been tossing restlessly in her borrowed bed, the retrieval of her alarm clock had been the last thing on her mind.

She wondered if Dan was one of those health-conscious fanatics who believed in consuming food before noon. Worse yet, he might be one of those archaic males who expected it to be provided for him.

She hoped not. For one thing, there simply wasn't time, and for another, Shelly was not big on the thought of cracking, or smelling, a raw egg anytime before one. She would, however, provide his morning fix of caffeine, if he was so addicted.

Time demons snapped at her conscious and she threw back the covers, grabbing for her robe. The wood-planked floor was cool under her bare feet as she raced from her brother's room. Passing the workroom, she tested the doorknob and finding it unlocked, she detoured into the kitchen for the key. A few moments later she was back.

"Dan! I'm late. If you want to come with me, you have to get up...now!" She pounded hard enough on the bedroom door that a neighbor, if she'd had one, would have heard her. "I'll put the coffee on. Use my bathroom, I'll use the one in the hall."

Not waiting for a response, she pivoted on her heel and sprinted for the kitchen. It was even later than she'd thought it to be. Shelly took a look at the bold-faced clock ticking quietly on the wall and grabbed for the teakettle. No time for the good stuff; instant would have to do. She reached for the jar she kept on the back shelf. Dan would have to dump the crystals into a mug all by himself. Filling the kettle with water, she put it on to heat.

Fifteen minutes later, showered, shampooed and wet, she belted her robe one more time. She'd remembered to take a change of clothes out of her room before giving it over to her guest the night before, but she couldn't finish dressing without underwear, and she wouldn't stop dripping without a hair dryer. Again she dashed down the hall and pounded on the door.

"Dan, get decent...I need some things from my bathroom." Giving him an impatient five seconds to respond, she lifted her fists to pound again. "Dan!"

"I was under the impression," Dan drawled as he came from the kitchen to the top of the hall, "that women preferred indecent men." A smile lit his eyes as he leaned his shoulder against the wall, watching her over the rim of a mug as he lifted it to his mouth.

Shelly came to a slamming halt. She had been so busy fighting last night that she'd forgotten how stomach-drop gorgeous the man was. Some men were like that, a surprise each time you saw them, an assault on the female nervous system.

No one had a right to look that good in the morning. His eyes weren't bloodshot, full of grit and restless dreams. They were full of what looked like indulgence, heavy lidded and lazy. Like her, he wasn't completely dressed yet, but on him, the lack of a top covering was a visual feast, not a necessity. Fine, dark curls stretched across taut, well-defined chest muscles, then arrowed down his flat belly to cluster around his navel, disappearing under the top button of his fly. His hair was mussed as if he'd simply run his fingers through it instead of a comb, and his white teeth flashed decadently through the stubble of his morning beard.

Why, she wondered miserably, did he have to look like that? Why did his body have to be so long and lean? What was behind the quirk to his lazy smile that suggested he knew answers to secrets she couldn't begin to guess? In comparison, she felt the sharp sting of her own inadequacies.

She hadn't taken the time to wrap a towel around her hair, and it hung in heavy, wet strands, plastered to her skull, dripping down her neck. Her feet were bare, her robe was old, and she'd put nothing on her face but soap and moisturizer.

"Do you—" Her question started out too high and reedy. She had to clear her throat, back up and start again. "Do you always look like this in the morning?"

Dan gave a faint, questioning shrug. "'Fraid so."

As she smiled grimly, the remaining breath in Shelly's lungs left in a short spurt of resignation. "I thought as much," she said slowly, then reluctantly walked up the hall until she was close enough to touch him. She stood looking up at him for a long minute, letting him look at her, as well. "And now you know."

A smile pulled at Dan's mouth. "What do I know?"

Shelly spoke slowly and precisely. "That I always look—" she made a vague sweeping gesture down her person "—like this in the morning." Both hands went to the belt of her robe, and she gave the ends a self-conscious tug. "It's probably best you discovered it early on." She smiled lamely. "If you want to call off negotiations, I won't hold it against you."

Dan shook his head in amused exasperation. He moved closer still, lessening the remaining gap her hesitation kept between them. "Shelly," he chided, gently cupping her face in his hands, "that won't work. You see—" he bent his head "—I think short, barefooted, women—" he brushed one light, teasing kiss across her nose "—with soggy red hair—" another kiss landed on the trio of freckles along her cheekbone, the third one brushing softly against the corner of her mouth "—are wildly sexy."

His breath smelled of coffee, and his skin of soap. If she moved her head the slightest fraction of an inch, he'd share the sensual pleasure of his mouth with her. Helplessly, Shelly reached up to grasp his wrists so that she could remain upright. He was doing it to her again! She closed her eyes against him, but he was too close, his effect too immediate.

"It doesn't go away." His whisper fell across her face, soft and warm. "I tried... when I didn't hear from you, I tried damned hard. That's why I came, Shelly Barker."

"There's more to life than hormones," she whispered in confusion. She didn't like the way her heart slammed against her ribs or the giddy excitement she felt from the touch of his hands. Those things had a way of clouding a woman's mind, affecting her judgment. "Every law in the universe says you shouldn't be here. You should be satisfied with your well-ordered life back in Denver. Why did you have to come around to interfere in mine?"

"Why are you so determined to keep me out of it? What, exactly, is your life like?"

The persistence in his voice made her want to stamp her foot in frustration. The gentleness made her throat ache. She pulled back her shoulders. She thought of her work schedule, the bizarre hours, the frenetic pace. "Hectic," she told him. Her brother sprang instantly to mind. "Crazy...sometimes." Then she swallowed painfully as she considered her isolation up high on her hill. "Lonely."

"You said you were going to share it with me this weekend," he quietly reminded her. "Come on, darlin', show me the dragons."

Her frown got worse before it got better. "I did." She nodded. "I will." Stepping back, she broke contact with him. "But when you've had enough, let me know."

Dan's smile tilted quizzically. "Why does that have the ring of challenge to it?"

Shelly stopped at her bedroom door. "It wasn't meant to," she told him soberly. "What I'm giving you is an out...when you're ready."

"What do you have...elves at the bottom of your garden? Who shoveled the driveway?"

Clicking her seat belt into place, Shelly turned her head and grinned. She waited until Dan fastened his before shifting the Bronco into reverse, giving all her attention to backing out from the long, narrow driveway and navigating around his rental car.

"Nothing magic about it," she said finally. "It's strictly a free-enterprise transaction. The kid in this house shovels." Pulling to a slow stop in front of a mailbox one street over and down from her own, she opened the door of the mailbox, deposited a sealed envelope and drove on. "I pay him. Which reminds me," she said, just as if one thing had to do with another, "what's going to happen to the Lincoln?"

"By the time we get back, it should be sitting in your driveway, washed, waxed and rechromed."

She laughed. "Such is the power of the gold credit card, hmm?"

"Strictly a free-enterprise transaction."

Dan stretched easily in the bucket seat. The weather did nothing to contribute to the smile on his face. He hadn't seen the sun since he'd left Tampa, and according to the weather man, another storm front was on its way.

He should have been home collecting his laurels for the job he'd completed down South. Some people were bound to be impressed with his handling of the McIvor deal. They would appreciate the months of negotiations Dan alone had had to put in because his Cousin Kiall simply hadn't the interest or attention span for that kind of sustained battle. When his Cousin Ty had been too inflexible to yield, it was Dan who had moved toward compromise.

The proof of his success was in a signed deed to a piece of property now residing in the family treasury.

He had single-handedly expanded the economy base, struck a mighty blow for capitalism, made the IRS deliriously happy and financed a new BMW for each of his sisters, not to mention college tuition for his future children. But was Shelly Barker making the appropriate gushing noises? Was she standing back in awe?

Dan moved again to a more comfortable position, folded his arms across his chest and slanted a glance at the small woman in the driver's seat. She was leaning forward, concentrating so fiercely on the snow-packed roads that her nose barely missed the steering wheel. Was she impressed with his deeds of boardroom skill and cunning?

Not likely, he thought dryly, and the smile edging his mouth stretched to a grin. She'd calmly informed him that she would drive this morning because, as she'd put it, *she* knew where they were going. He'd yet to detect one trace of reverence in her voice. He'd just secured a valuable piece of property, landmarking the next Sutherland resort complex, and she had it firmly fixed in her mind that he wouldn't suit her. Hell, she was still trying to talk him off her hill.

"That smile," Shelly said, noting his snapping white teeth and humorously narrowed eyes, "looks suspicious." Since the traffic light was red, she had time to give him her full attention. "I don't trust it."

"This smile is something I always put on my face when I'm hungry...you have heard of breakfast, haven't you, Shelly? It's a thing one does before lunch."

"I'd hoped it wouldn't come to this," she said, suddenly deciding to take the time, even if it cost her. For the day she had planned, it would be best for all of them if Dan started out on a full stomach. "I'll pull under somebody's arch for you. Just one thing, though." Her voice was pleasantly civil.

"If you order anything remotely yellow or slimy, all bets in this deal are off."

"I know we're going somewhere." Ignoring Shelly's look of fascinated horror, the same look she'd been wearing since he'd ordered the waffles, Dan forked the last of his meal into his mouth. "And I know we're in a hurry to get there. So I guess my question is, where are we going?"

Shelly blinked. He'd taken the hint about ordering eggs for breakfast, but as she watched, she'd come to the conclusion that dough slathered in syrup was only one level up from atrocity.

"We...ah..." She cleared her throat, focusing her attention away from the deliberate act he was committing. "We have a lot to do today. My brother's annual Christmas party is tonight, and I promised I'd take him shopping. We're on our way to pick him up. He wants a new suit...something *GQ*-ish to impress the ladies. And we'll need gifts, all three of us." Crossing her arms, she rested her elbows on the Formica table. "That is if you want to come—to the party I mean. Everyone has to bring a small gift to exchange."

"You're going to your brother's Christmas party?"

"I have to," she said, and shrugged lamely. "I'm the refreshment committee for his group home."

"I'd forgotten Christmas was less than three weeks away." Dan wondered at her odd hesitation. Would his presence at an event that had already been planned put her in an awkward position? "Do you have a date...is that why you aren't enthusiastic about me tagging along?"

Startled, she shook her head. "No, it's nothing like that. I hadn't planned on taking one, but dates are fine. It's just that..." She looked at the hangnail on her thumb and decided to leave it—she might need it for nibbling another time. "This isn't going to be the kind of party you're used to. The people aren't sophisticated. Nothing alcoholic is ever served and—"

"Shelly," Dan said, interrupting gently, "do you think I'm so much of a jerk that those things would matter?"

"I don't know," she admitted in a small voice, looking at the hangnail again. No, she decided, not yet.

"Then—" he reached across the table for her restless hand "—I guess you'll just have to find out. What time is the party?"

"Seven... it starts at seven."

"What else is on your agenda?" He gave the hand he held a squeeze before letting it go.

She looked up and smiled. "Shopping at the mall, and finding a Christmas tree. I promised my brother we'd pick out the tree this weekend."

Dan shrugged. "That doesn't sound like a heavy schedule."

"Are you kidding?" Shelly laughed in disbelief. "Three weeks before Christmas? It's going to take all day, if we can find a parking space. Dan?" Her gaze dipped to the plate on the table in front of him, and she shuddered. "Just a word of caution... my brother is... can be difficult if he thinks his position in my life is threatened. He won't like you, but that's because, well, that's my fault. If... when you're ready to bail out, I promise there will be no hard feelings."

## *Chapter Seven*

From the restaurant, Shelly drove cautiously to the west side of the valley and turned off from the mainstream of traffic into a residential section tucked neatly away behind a large medical complex. After twisting through a maze of streets, she brought the Bronco to a halt in the driveway of a sprawling, red-brick house.

"Interesting place," Dan muttered, taking in the haphazard architecture of the building. There were two separate additions to the original structure that he could see, possibly more that he could not. Someone must have decided that space came before asthetics.

Shelly exhaled a long breath. She forced her fingers to loosen their death grip on the steering wheel and turned with determined brightness. "About four years ago, this place was renovated to serve as a group home for disabled adults. Staff, mostly students from the university, are paid to supervise the residents living here and maintain the building. This particular home is run as a shift model."

She knew she sounded stilted, like a new tour guide, and cleared her throat before continuing. "Which means that instead of having group home 'parents,' a couple who act as surrogate family and live with the residents, the staff comes in on a rotating basis. My brother has lived here for about three and a half years now."

"Was it your idea to... did you..."

Her expression was quiet and her eyes were direct as she finished the question. "Was it my decision to take my mentally retarded—and deaf—brother from his own home, away from everything familiar, and abandon him to the care of paid, rotating strangers?" Not knowing what else to do with her hands, she fumbled the keys from the ignition. "Yes."

"Shelly," Dan said just as quietly, putting a large hand over her much smaller, restless one, "don't flog yourself on my account. I'm sure you did what you had to."

Dan was too good, giving her credit where none was due. There was no way to explain that she'd done the right thing for the wrong reason. No one knew how much the decision had cost her. Even after a year and a half, she still paid.

"Is someone always around?"

"Staff, you mean?" Looking back at the house, she pointed to the second story. "Someone always is, yes. There has to be. Twelve people live here... all of them mentally retarded, all of them hearing impaired to one degree or another. We'd better go in. Richard Robert expected me an hour ago."

Even though Shelly had given Dan a quick sketch on what to expect, he was unprepared for the sights and smells as he followed her into the house. Not that they were offensive smells or unpleasant sights, just different.

A world away from what he was used to.

The scent of fish from a recent meal lingered, not quite masked by baking cake and pine disinfectant. Pages of the newspaper lay under a slumbering body, both scattered across the living room carpet. Another body sat hunched, back to the door, three inches from the earsplitting blast of Saturday-morning cartoon characters on a wide-screen TV.

From deeper in the house came the droning of a vacuum cleaner and the pounding bass of hard-rock music. Somewhere in the near vicinity, a telephone demanded attention. Across the wide room, a thin, fortyish woman vigorously kept a rocking chair in motion while working on some kind of needlecraft project spread across her lap.

Most of the occupants of the room were oblivious as Shelly and Dan passed through. The woman in the rocking chair looked up, but aside from a startling, toothless grin and a strange gesture with her hands, no other response was given.

Dan had to ask, "How can she concentrate with that racket blasting in her ear?" He looked at the sleeping male body on the floor and shrugged in amazement. He wasn't even going to question how that was possible.

Shelly turned her head back and up. "Because she can't hear it," she told him, raising her own voice to be heard. "Mavis is deaf. David—" she waved toward the body in front of the TV "—can hear some things...Mavis nothing."

Turning her attention to the woman in question, Shelly did something graceful and quick with her hands. Then it was Mavis's turn. Whatever she did brought a sudden gurgle of laughter from Shelly.

Dan knew what it was, he had even seen it used before, but again, he had to ask, "That's sign language, right? You're talking to her?"

Shelly nodded. "You see, the rule is Mavis has to wear her dentures when she's out in the community or when she wants to meet people coming into the house. They call it 'being socially appropriate.' When I asked if she wanted to meet you, she said she did, but not enough that she's willing to put her teeth in."

At Dan's dawning look of chagrin, Shelly took his hand and gave it a comforting squeeze. "Don't take it personally. There was a fact-finding committee from the governor's office here not so long ago, on one of those election-year tours. Mavis didn't get the denture cream out for them, either. Come on, someone should be in the kitchen."

A man was. He turned, gave a pointed look at the clock and flashed Shelly a scowl. The look changed to a knowing smirk when he saw Dan. "Hi, Shell, overslept a bit this morning, hmm?"

Mavis, Shelly thought sourly, wasn't the only one in the house who could do with some social-appropriateness training. Sometimes young Chad could be as subtle as cork.

"Dan," she said, beginning the introduction, "this is Chad Gibson. He makes up a part of the weekend crew. Chad, this is Dan."

The younger man made brief eye contact, lifting his hand in acknowledgment. Nervously, Shelly looked around the room. "I'll run up and see what's keeping Richard Robert." She stopped long enough to give Dan a reassuring smile. "This will only take a minute."

After a lengthy perusal of the room itself, Dan turned his attention to the younger man. Jamming his hands into the pockets of his trousers, he took a curious step forward.

"Brownies," Chad Gibson muttered. Pulling two oblong pans from the oven, he sat them on towels spread over the counter, put two more pans in and dropped the oven mitts. "Mint... for the party tonight."

"Oh." Dan nodded. It was the first time he'd ever witnessed a man with twenty-pound arm muscles making mint brownies. Not that there was anything wrong with a defensive linebacker making brownies, it was just...unexpected. As unexpected as the snake tattoo, triple-pierced ear and gingham apron.

"You going?"

Dan shook his rambling thoughts away. "To the party? I'm taking Shelly, yes."

Chad grunted while reaching up for a mixing bowl high in the cupboard. He went on to dump two pouches of instant frosting into the bowl. "Shell's a classy lady. She does a lot around here that she doesn't have to...you know, time, money."

Dan thought that sounded like Shelly. He had discovered that given the right circumstances, she could be generous to a fault. He was curious to know more about this house and, indirectly, Shelly. "How long have you worked here?"

"A little over three years now." Chad looked up from his task. Youth fell away from the smooth face, replaced with a very hard, adult concern. "Shelly Barker is a friend of mine. The last man she brought around gave her nothing but grief. Sure would be a shame if another...*friend* decided the ride was too rough...after he'd led her down the road."

Dan absorbed the comment. His impulse was to bite back, sharp and quick. He drew a rough, irritated breath. His relationship with Shelly Barker was none of this post-pubescent hulk's business. His mouth opened, and it remained open, but words never got past his lips.

A low, keening bellow rent the air, followed by a split second of stunning silence. In the next heartbeat, a connecting door shuddered on its hinges as it crashed back against the wall.

"Uh-oh," Chad mumbled.

A slender, dark-haired young man exploded into the room, bringing the screech of Nike crosstrainers with him as he slammed past Dan and skidded to a halt. He whirled back around and Dan was then subjected to a curious, four-second inspection before the young man lost interest and his attention focused on the cooling brownie pans. He inched his way closer, making odd snuffling noises as he gestured wildly. As soon as his hand got too close to the first pan, it was pushed away.

He approached the second pan and was again patiently but firmly turned aside. Frustrated, he took a step back and opened his mouth. The noise that issued from his throat had the fast, staccato rhythm of a rusty hydraulic machine.

Chad did not look up. He continued to spread frosting, as if having a man garble in his face was something that happened every day. Calmly, over the noise, he explained, "Richy wants a brownie."

Dan's astonished mind boggled. "Why," he asked blankly, "don't you give him one?"

Chad glanced up. "I can tell you're new at this, so let me explain. Richy has the mind of a small child, but he is a grown man. Giving him a brownie would only prove that being loud and obnoxious is the way to get what he wants. Besides, these are for the party. He knows that."

Intellectually, Richy may have known there was a special purpose for the brownies. However, judging by the increasing decibel level of the demand, he was having a difficult time accepting the fact emotionally.

Then, as Dan watched, the noise ended.

But not the scene.

Richy spun, looked at Dan, hard, then threw himself into the nearest chair. Another furtive glance at Dan and then Richy's head dived to his knees, and he burst into wet, shoulder-shaking tears.

Dan found himself patting his pants pockets, looking for keys to a car parked high on the other side of the valley. Even though Richy's second glance had clued Dan that this performance was mainly for his benefit, it still unnerved him to see a grown man sobbing his heart out. "He, ah, he's quite an operator."

Chad grinned quizzically. "Didn't take you long to catch on, or were you warned?" He watched Richy for a moment and shook his head, "Tears have got to be the oldest con in the guy's routine."

Shifting from one foot to the other, Dan cleared his throat. "There's more?"

"Richy wouldn't be the man he is unless he tried. This morning I explained, and everyone agreed, that the brownies were for the party. But Richy's the kind of guy that never thinks the rules should apply to him. In his other life, he would have been a politician."

Out of his own element and knowing it, Dan waited for Chad to do something about the sobbing young man. "How long," he asked finally, wondering what the hell was keeping Shelly, "can he keep this up?"

"That's hard to say." Chad rubbed the side of his nose with a knuckle. "He has been known to go right to the floor with the heel-kicking, fist-banging-type stuff. This could swing that way or last only seconds . . . until he decides this isn't the way to get . . . ah, there, see?"

As swiftly as the tears had come, they were gone. With a brief flash of a wide smile, Richy was up from the table and again at the counter. This time his snuffling noise lacked the demanding quality, and he used his hands, not wildly, but to communicate.

"Now he's got it," Chad said, reaching in a drawer for a knife. The confection was hot enough to be sticky as he cut into it, placed a cut square on a piece of paper towel and handed it to the waiting man.

Dan thought he understood and he approved, but he had to clarify. "He still got what he wanted, but he did it right this time, right?"

"Yeah. My job is to help him learn, not to play hardball over a few lousy brownies. Uh—" Chad's gaze slid past Dan to the door "—I'd move out of the line of traffic if I were you. No matter how he did it, Richy still scored, and we should be hearing from the other residents—" a heavy thump sounded from somewhere deeper in the house "—any minute now."

Mavis was the first one in, not even stopping to acknowledge Dan's presence as she made her way to the cooling pans. Judging by her sharp gesturing, she was not pleased with the breach in kitchen security. Clutching his loot, Richy sidled away from Chad, slipping over to and then behind Dan. Mavis turned and began to stalk.

The kitchen door swung open.

Dan swallowed.

A second, irate protester entered the fray, but Dan's concern was more immediate. Mavis was a tall woman, nearly tall enough to meet him nose to nose. He took a step back. She took one forward. She made rapid gestures. He shrugged helplessly. She gestured again, adding a sharp grunting sound that came from deep in her throat. He hadn't the faintest clue.

How could he explain his innocent part in the program when he couldn't speak the language? The door opened again, admitting several more rioters. Meanwhile, the culprit, Richy, had moved up, very close, behind Dan. So close that when Dan considered retreat, he could feel the smaller man's breathing hot between his shoulder blades.

"There you are! I've been looking all over the house for...what is going on in here?"

Dan decided he'd never heard a sweeter sound in his life. Pride refused to let him grab Shelly and use her as a shield, but he couldn't cover his gasp of relief as she entered the kitchen.

"Dan?" Shelly prodded.

"Brownies," he said. He would have finished the story, except... "She's sniffing me," he said, his voice a thin, calm thread of its normally deeper tones. "A moment ago she was using her hands, calling me all kinds of a fool, and now she's sniffing my neck. Doesn't she need her teeth in to do this? Shelly, why is Mavis smelling my neck?"

"Believe me—" Shelly's tone was absent as she assessed the cacophony of sights and sounds in the room "—half the civilized women in the world would nuzzle your neck if they could. What's going on in here? Mavis, quit now, I know it smells good, but that's mine. Chad?"

Dan did the only thing he possibly could do to save his neck for his own true love and to end the scene. He reached for Mavis's chin, tilted it up and shook his head in the universal message, *Nothin' doin', sweetheart.* With her nose out of his neck, he firmly moved Mavis back three steps.

"We had a slight misunderstanding over the brownies," Dan said. Giving Chad a hard, direct look, he added, "Distribute the rest of what's in the pan...and see that Mavis gets a big piece. I'll buy a case of the things for the party tonight."

"You don't have to do that."

"I want to," Dan insisted, and the patience in his voice said it would be dangerous to argue. "Now—" he slanted a glance at Shelly "—if you'll collect your brother, I'd like to meet him and then leave."

Shelly went still. "Dan?" Her smile was feeble and slipped. "You *have* met my brother."

Reaching around, she snagged an arm and pulled the attached body forward for presentation. "I don't know what you've done, but behave yourself now, Richard Robert." She spoke aloud and used her hands to sign the words. "I mean it, Richy. Please just say hello."

Gripping the steering wheel, Shelly moved her shoulders in a quick, restless gesture. If Dan didn't break his silence soon, they might not make it to the mall. She was a competent driver, but she also had the practice of foreshadow and worry down to an art. The thing was, on these roads, at this minute, she could do one effectively, but not both.

She wished Dan would say something...*anything*... but after his initial, futile attempts to communicate with Richard Robert, he'd gone quiet. Odd how even rational, levelheaded people were guilty of doing inane, nonsensical things, like turning up the volume while grotesquely mouthing words to a man who could neither speak, read nor hear.

It was difficult enough to concentrate on the slippery roads without having a brooding, silent man sitting next to her. For the second time since the introduction, Shelly found herself dreading but wanting to know what thoughts ran through Dan's mind.

The first time had been back at the group home as Richard Robert offered a guileless smile along with a sticky handshake. Confusion had played across Dan's face. Strange how the friendliest smile could turn from easy to...awkward. The strongest, deepest eyes could slide away in confusion.

Why, she wondered, did Richard Robert have to pick the most inconvenient times to be...Richy.

Dan had looked at that sticky hand for a long moment, then into the bright blue eyes. Then he'd looked at Shelly.

Shelly had forced herself to look away. She couldn't guide Dan, and she refused to apologize or offer explanations.

She determined to wait it out, sitting patiently through one stop light, then another. From the back seat, Richard Robert's monotone, "ba-ba-hum," sounded loud in the enclosed confines. A snowplow with a severe exhaust problem rumbled past, splashing heavy sludge onto the side window of the Bronco. The disappointment of having expected more from Dan Sutherland flashed in and out of her mind.

The first time he'd reached out to touch her hair, in his aunt's kitchen, she'd known this was a bad idea.

"Why didn't you tell me?"

"What?" Dan's quiet accusation hit her, startling her out of her mental wanderings. "What was I supposed to tell you?"

His scowl was quick and fierce, lasting only a moment before he let out a controlled breath. "That because some other jerk let you down, this whole weekend is set up to be a kind of test... and you don't expect me to pass, either."

Her astonishment was complete. Unthinkingly, she made the signal and pulled into the mall's parking lot. She caught her lip between her small, white teeth and started to speak, but no words came out.

All her thoughts had been centered around Dan's reaction to and the eventual defense of her brother. Her mind was blank. What did Spencer have to do with this?

"There's one... a parking space, two rows over and down," Dan directed easily, watching the play of emotions flit across her expressive features. Her eyes could change color, he noticed, pale blue into gray when she was calm, a darker bluish green when she was upset... or aroused. He smiled into them. "Maybe now isn't the best time to start this particular conversation. Park the car, Shelly, you're blocking traffic."

Christmas carols greeted their ears as shoppers rushed through the entrance doors. Excited children whined and babbled, urging their parents toward Santa Claus in center court. Crowds marched shoulder to shoulder while lights glittered from artificial trees and elves danced from display windows.

Dan knew his jaw had dropped when Shelly snapped her fingers under his nose. "When was the last time you did your own Christmas shopping?" she asked, laughing up at him.

He knew what she expected him to say, that he didn't do anything so mundane as his own shopping, and if he did, it was never anywhere as average as a mall. The truth was, he did do his own gift choosing from a few select stores in Denver and normally, he had the job finished by October. But because he was fascinated by the sparkling eyes and soft mouth laughing up at him, he didn't bother defending himself.

"Let's just say it's been a while."

"Okay," she agreed easily, and in her excitement, she caught at his hand. "Think of it, Dan. Can you imagine what this must be like for Richard Robert?" She waved toward her wide-eyed brother standing in front of a twinkling window display. "With no auditory stimulation, he gets his input visually. This is a feast for him . . . the lights, the colors. He can't get enough. Everywhere he turns there's more."

Dan followed the movement of her hand. Staring into the window with the uninhibited delight of a child was a rumpled, bone-thin man of less than medium height. One of his hands was on the glass, as if he would touch the animated scene inside. His rapid hums were high, breathy sounds of excitement.

As Dan watched, he noticed shoppers go out and around rather than pass close to the strange-sounding young man. There were outright stares, quick furtive glances and whispers of curiosity. When Shelly went over to lead Richard Robert to the next window, she came under the same scrutiny.

Something else occurred to Dan. He saw the enjoyment of her brother's awe reflected in Shelly's expression as she walked back to Dan. He had to wonder what the responsibility was like for her.

"Tell me about Richy."

"It's Richard Robert," she corrected with a smile. "Only when he's being manipulative is he Richy." She went quiet for a moment, thinking over Dan's question. She had a pat answer to give; she knew it by rote. "I can give you a medical explanation of *why* he is like he is." She shrugged.

"Clinically, he's classified as 'severely retarded with an absolute hearing loss.' He can feel some things, and he thinks he hears—vibrations mostly, explosions." She smiled sadly. "He has other physical problems along with the deafness. Neurological damage that affects his large muscles and accounts for his shuffling gait."

It was an impressive list, but Richard Robert was more than a category of physical deficiencies. There were so many things mere words wouldn't explain. "I can't *tell* you what it's like. I can say that life is never dull. But..." Again she shrugged. "You'll just have to follow along and experience Richard Robert for yourself. That is, if you still want to go through with this."

Dan saw the hesitation in her eyes. It was a look that questioned but would accept his answers with complete neutrality. He wondered what kind of an ass this other guy had been, and he felt an irrational surge of anger. He acknowledged that he may have a few faults, but he'd be damned before he would stand accountable for someone else's.

His voice was soft and a shade menacing. "Do you think after all this, I'd duck out because your brother is mentally retarded?"

Casting a watchful eye toward the object of their discussion, she turned back to Dan. "No more so than I would duck out because your mother is a tyrant," she said tartly, carefully adjusting the shoulder strap of her leather bag. "I'm not questioning your humanity, Dan."

"What *is* the question?"

Her gaze met his with watchful wariness. "Have you...do you know many people with severe disabilities?"

"I know..." What did he know? Pitifully little, Dan thought in disgust. He knew flu—Hong Kong, Asian and Type A. He knew about colds and broken bones, but the function of his body and mind had always been his to control. His family contributed hundreds of thousands of dollars a year to charities. He had seen and been moved by the telethon kids on TV, and the company made an issue of nondiscrimination hiring. He made the right moves and the right noises. "I know nothing," he finally admitted starkly. "I haven't got a clue."

"That's what I thought." She shook her hair back from her face. "So I guess my question is, are you sure? Are you positive you want to learn? Please, be honest."

"At this point," Dan said bluntly, "I'm not positive about anything but getting you into bed." At her startled gasp, he gave her a long, slow smile. "For the male, bed is generally the initial goal in any relationship. If you haven't figured that out, then I guess there are things we both can learn."

As he took her arm to lead her through the crowd, another smile played around his mouth. "One last question," he said, waiting until she looked up at him. "Why didn't you tell me your brother was—"

"Mentally retarded?" She stiffened, clipping off the words. "Deaf?"

Dan gave her a short, level stare. "My question was," he corrected calmly, "and I'm referring to that stunt he pulled back in the kitchen, why didn't you tell me your brother was a terrorist from hell?"

The defensiveness left Shelly's rigid spine. Her closed fists uncurled, finger by finger, until she could feel them separately. A spurt of laughter bubbled in her throat. "He is good, isn't he?"

Dan nodded. "I've yet to see his equal."

Approaching Richard Robert, she reached out to redirect his attention. "Oh, you haven't seen anything yet," she told Dan. Again she laughed, but only as a release from tension. "He gets much better."

She crossed her fingers as they moved down the mall. Dan had taken the first step down the Barkers' yellow brick road with more charm and humor than she'd expected. But her brother was, indeed, a master of surprises, and the weekend was young.

## *Chapter Eight*

Normally, Dan directed events to suit himself or to allow him to be an active participant. Yet in this situation, since his ignorance was a given, he was relegated to a passive position. And, at first, the role of observer sat oddly with him as he moved through the day with Shelly and Richard Robert.

Perhaps the need to accustom himself to the unexpected part pushed some sort of Pause button on his reasoning ability. Or perhaps he simply wasn't as quick as he'd always thought he was. Whatever the delay in his thought process, it took a while to figure out that there was going to be more to the day than a simple shopping trip.

Richard Robert ran ahead, moving from here to there quickly, then on to something else. Shelly followed with Dan, but kept her brother under surveillance. No mother ever kept a sharper eye tuned to her charge. No federal agent could have been more subtle in the doing of it.

"Why don't you just keep him with you?" Dan questioned at one point. "At this rate you'll wear yourself out."

Shelly looked up in surprise. "I can't tie him to me as if he were a toddler. He's twenty-five years old."

Dan made a production of clearing his throat, carefully pointing out what he thought was obvious. "You haven't once let him out of your sight. What's the difference?"

With a shrug that said she had never given it conscious thought, Shelly tried to explain. "On the one hand, Richard Robert is as independent as he possibly can be, and I want that for him." She paused a moment to think through the flip side. "But he still needs to be guided...protected from situations he finds—or creates—that he can't understand or deal with. So I try not to hover or be too obvious about what I'm doing, but I do watch him."

Hesitating, she searched Dan's dark eyes. "In his head he has all the mischief and curiosity of a six-year-old, but he *is* a man. Does that make sense?"

What made sense to Dan were the three golden freckles growing more prominent across her pretty little nose as the strain of her balancing act took its toll. They had been at this window peering for close to an hour, and not once had she relaxed enough to enjoy it for herself. Richard Robert, Dan decided, had the edge on this round.

And it was a contest, he thought later. Bell number two rang the moment Shelly started maneuvers toward the department store. Richard Robert did not fall immediately to the ground with heels kicking, but only because Shelly seemed sharply emphatic with what she signed.

"Is he going to cry?" Dan suffered a few bad moments over the possibility of a scene like the one back in the group home's kitchen. It might have helped if he understood what was going on. All he could do was stand by while Richard Robert made the most godawful, pitiable noises and signed with frantic, jerky gestures. Shelly, arms folded, held firm. Around them, children goggled and mothers shushed, rushing them by.

"Shelly?" Dan asked again, swallowing, "are we talking right to the floor with this one?"

"Possibly," she answered bluntly, and for a moment her gaze left her brother, arcing to Dan. He looked the tiniest bit pale, and why not? After all these years, she still felt queazy when this kind of thing happened in public. This couldn't possibly be what Dan Sutherland was used to.

Yet he did not ease away, did not pretend he belonged somewhere else, with someone else. Instead, Dan took a step closer. Not his normally confident, man-in-charge step, but a move all the same. That door Shelly kept barred opened again, wider, this time.

"What is it he wants?" At this point, Dan could have been persuaded to give Richard Robert Barker just about anything in his power to hand over.

"He wants to see Santa."

"Why don't we just walk over there?"

"You don't understand...he wants to *see* Santa. I am not going to stand in a two-hour line so that this man can sit on another man's lap."

Realizing he'd exhausted one resource, Richard Robert ruthlessly turned to Dan. Dan had never considered himself a squeamish man, but he found himself edging back against the glass outside an athletic-shoe store.

"All the experts say you have to start as though you mean to go on," Shelly cautioned softly. "He's testing you. He's spoiled, and I did it, but, Dan, if you give in on this one, Richy's got you."

Dan never took his eyes off those slender, waving hands. Fatalistically, he wondered how much time he had before Richy got tired of the preliminary skirmish and pulled out... *the big one.*

"Ah, Shelly." He cleared his throat, hoping to rid his voice of the scratchy note of panic. "I don't know what to do."

"Unless you're willing to stand in line with Richy for two hours—and remember, you'll be surrounded by thousands of teething babies and maniacal toddlers—tell him no. Here, watch me for a minute." She held up her hand, bringing the first two fingers and thumb together. "That's all it takes to say no. The choice is yours."

Dan looked into Richy's moist, pleading blue eyes. He saw the line of shrieking, impatient children stretched out and beyond the turn in the mall, and he realized how completely out of place Richy would be in that line. "Sorry, pal," he said softly, making the sign. "No."

He was fully prepared for Richy's immediate dive to the floor, but incredibly, nothing happened. Richard Robert stared hard for a long moment, perhaps to test Dan's determination. Then he signed something, first to Dan, then to Shelly. Shelly made a sharp counterpoint and ended by folding her arms firmly across her chest. Richard Robert concluded with a few swift gestures aimed at Dan and stepped back.

Frustrated, Dan looked to Shelly. "What did you say? Hell! What did he say?"

"Richy isn't pleased with our decision."

"I gathered that much." Dan's mouth twisted. "I want to know what that bit at the end was about. It had to do with me. What was it?"

Shelly bit her lip. Judging by the stubborn set of Dan's jaw, she decided it wouldn't do much good to hedge. "He's not happy that I brought you along. He says you're mean, and he called you a name. I told him to knock it off. That if he wanted to get the tree today and a new suit for the party, he'd better come quietly. In essence, he said okay."

"That's all?" Dan's relief was monumental. "It was that easy?"

The blue of Shelly's eyes glowed bluer with amusement. She turned toward the department store's entrance. "Sometimes it is," she told him, and her grin tilted. "Sometimes it isn't."

Dan's curiosity got the best of him. "What name did he use, Shelly?"

"It doesn't matter."

"The name, darlin'. I'm a big boy, I can take it."

Shelly finally lifted her head, and her eyes were round and solemn. "He called you a farthead. Ah, here we are...suits coming up. Richard! I wish you'd stay with me."

Dan Sutherland, of the Denver branch of Sutherlands, opened his mouth, then closed it on a nonplussed snap. He had been described as many things over the years—ruthless bastard, cunning devil, shrewd businessman, even a spoiled playboy. He followed the Barkers, mouthing this new description of himself "Farthead?"

"That's what he said." Shelly bit her lip, sparing him one last glance. "An old one."

Round three presented itself close to the clearance rack in the young men's department.

"I don't believe," Dan said carefully, watching Richard Robert methodically examine every seam in the unfortunate jacket he'd discovered, "I've ever seen that exact shade of green before."

"Umm, green isn't what I had in mind," Shelly confessed, eyeing the jacket with a kind of horrified fascination. "I thought something in a more dignified navy or black."

"Richard Robert has a unique sense of style." Dan racked his memory, but could not come up with a time he'd ever seen a wool suit coat in a military camouflage color.

"One of a kind," Shelly agreed. "He always did like to make his own statement."

Had Dan been the sort of man to keep a journal or one to write chatty letters home, he would have begun the entry, *December 7: Today I've seen things I've never seen before.*

He would have recorded the scene that took place in Mervyn's department store with the sure knowledge that truth was, indeed, stranger than fiction. Of course, not being able to speak the language, he had missed the fine details. For instance, he never understood exactly what method Shelly used to induce Richard Robert away from the green suit. But he had his theories.

Some might have called it compromise. Shelly paid for a dignified navy blue suit, just as she wanted. Richard Robert's unique sense of fashion was appeased with an unforgettably bright tie...a silk-screened, blue-red-and-green fishhead tie.

To all intents, the incident ended in a win-win draw. Dan kept his suspicions to himself. He might not have understood the quick exchange of signing that flew back and forth, but he'd seen the calculation in Shelly's eyes during negotiations. The softly spoken, so elusive Ms. Barker had unearthed that tie from an odds-and-end table to use as bribery, pure and blatant.

Then came the tree. Dan shuddered, shifting his shoulder to lean more comfortably against the wall as he thought about that episode. There were some things in a man's life better put behind him.

He stared out over the dance floor, watching the couples gyrate to the sixties tune blasting from the loudspeakers. He knew Shelly was around somewhere, but to find her would mean having to brave the gymnasium floor. It would take him a while to work up the nerve for another crossing.

True to Shelly's promise, Richard Robert's Christmas party was like none other Dan had ever attended. It wasn't so much the place—the hall was decorated in red-and-green crepe paper, with an artificial Christmas tree in the corner and a bright, glittering glass ball suspended in the middle of the dance floor. During his early school years, Dan had seen similar gymnasiums and decorations.

It wasn't the entertainment. No, Dan would have said that the holiday tunes belted out by the local high school chorale were interesting, but not unique. Nor was the visit from Santa Claus. At the Sutherland's last executive party, old Santa had been around to hand out the extravagant bonus checks. Dan smiled as he thought of it. His dad had looked rather distinguished in a white beard and red suit.

"Hi." Shelly approached the corner cautiously. She knew this had been a hell of a day for Dan. She stopped a few feet away, her eyes wide and wary as she ran her glance swiftly over his face and hair. "I'm sorry about the tree, Dan, honestly."

Dan shifted, making room for her. "Forget it, Shelly. You don't have to keep apologizing."

"I've never had one fall off the top of the car before. I swear the thing was strapped down tight. Lord, right there in the intersection, too. I've never heard so much rude honking. And then when we put it through the tailgate window, I had no idea pine could be so. . . leaky."

"No, problem." He managed, barely, not to growl.

"I should have thought to wrap something around the trunk. Should have put it through the back window like Richard Robert wanted to in the first place. At least it wouldn't have been wet and leaky." She glanced up again to his hair. "It looks like the worst of the pine tar is out."

Dan's scalp was still tingling from where he'd scrubbed. Odd, he thought, how those back inside knots in the strapping had come undone. Odder still had been the satisfied smile on Richard Robert's face when they stopped to fetch the tree from the middle of the slushy street.

That smile was something Dan was going to have to think about. "It's time to change the subject."

"Good idea," Shelly agreed brightly, and bit her lip. "Umm, why are you hiding in the corner? Are you bored with the party? Do you want to leave?"

Dan said nothing for a long moment. Slowly, a smile came to his mouth. "I'm pondering."

Shelly felt an almost dizzying relief. She'd been holding her breath for some kind of showdown ever since Richard Robert had undone the Christmas tree from the top of the car. She knew her brother had done it, and Dan Sutherland was many things, but he wasn't stupid. What surprised her was that Dan had stuck it out this long.

"What exactly—" she mimicked his smile and his drawl "—are you pondering?"

"Life." He nodded thoughtfully. "The odd twists and turns. I've just danced with the most beautiful little lady in a wheelchair. She tried to talk to me. I couldn't understand. The only part of her body she seemed to have control over was her smile." He shook his head, "And there I was, huffing and puffing down the back of her neck. My God, those electric wheelchairs are heavy! When the dance was over, she smiled and gurgled up at me. All I could do was wheeze."

"Oh, Dan," Shelly said. She sighed and started to laugh. "I hate to spoil your beatific mood, but it sounds to me as if you were dancing with Corrie. And it also sounds as if she was trying to tell you to take her brake off. You did release her chair brake, didn't you?"

"Brake?" he said slowly, blankly.

"On some chairs the break automatically comes on when the power is turned off. The only way to move the chair then, is to hit the button on the lever panel. Corrie can't do that for herself. You would have had to do it. No wonder you were puffing . . . no wonder she was laughing. You were trying to rock-and-roll with over two hundred pounds of dead weight."

Dan couldn't remember a time he'd felt so ridiculously idiotic. Unless it was earlier, when he'd been standing hip deep in the middle of a slushy intersection, collecting a soggy Christmas tree. Or minutes later when, in his rush to get back into the car, he found himself planted on top of the forgotten bakery box of brownies. With pine tar oozing down the side of his face and four dozen pastries smashed under his rear, he'd foolishly thought his comedy of errors had run its course.

He caught Shelly's hand. "Dance with me," he ordered softly, moving her right into his arms. For a moment he concentrated on the feel of her soft, slight body. For another moment, he blanked his mind, concentrating on nothing at all.

"I think," he said softly, slowly, "I overestimated my chances of acing your test. Do you remember those dragons you warned me about?"

"I remember."

"I haven't done such a great job in slaying them all. In fact, there were a couple I didn't see coming."

It took a lot for Dan to acknowledge his doubts, even more to admit them out loud. He was used to being in charge, couldn't remember a time he'd been so completely out of his element. Throughout the day, he'd felt as if he'd been upended and left reeling in a foreign land with unknown customs and incomprehensible rules.

He waited for a reaction, some comment from the woman in his arms, but he felt only the faint shrug of her shoulders, heard the quiet sigh.

"This isn't your world," she said at last. "I imagine you're used to parties a little different from this one."

"A bit," Dan agreed reflectively, bending his head to catch her murmured words. "Every year my mother orchestrates an intimate little gathering on Christmas Eve."

Shelly lifted her head from his shoulder and found herself smiling at the humor reflected in his musing tones. "As in Denver's finest?"

"Only the top one hundred or so. Any more and it couldn't be called 'intimate.'"

"Of course," she agreed with a faint laugh. "Tuxedos and jewels?"

"Hmm, more like black-tie and discreet glitter. The dazzle comes out for her New Year's bash."

Shelly couldn't help but grin. "I'll bet you do your fair share—of dazzling that is." Her expression sobered. "Of course, she expects you with her for these family dos?"

Dan nodded reluctantly. "She expects it, yes."

Shelly had thought as much and continued her line of thought. "She must be enormously proud of you, expecting the best of you . . . from you."

He had a good idea where this conversation was headed. She was going to tackle him with her, we're-from-different-worlds routine again, and since he had no inkling of what the answer would be once they got to the point, he decided evasive tactics were in order.

Her upturned face was so close, all he had to do was bend a bit to savor the lilting softness at the corner of her mouth. He felt her tremble and he pulled her closer. "Last year, she imported a chamber orchestra to belt out 'Jingle Bells' on violin and harp."

It seemed only right to give the delicate shell of her ear the same attention he'd given the corner of her mouth. "Why is it," he whispered, "I feel as if I've never tasted or held a woman before?"

"Battle fatigue. It affects certain people. Dan . . . ?" His name was a sighing whisper. If he didn't stop, her bones would dissolve. "Be serious, please. This is important."

"Darlin', you can't imagine how serious I am."

"No," she said, and shook her head. "Right now you're playing at distracting me—yourself from what's going on around us. Don't, it isn't fair."

His first instinct was to deny her accusation. His second was to question how she could so clearly see through him. To give himself time, he grasped at the first available straw.

"I've been meaning to ask you why the distinguished gentleman across the floor is wearing a football helmet with his dinner jacket. Not that it isn't a great helmet.... Broncos, isn't it?"

She didn't have to turn around to know whom he was referring to. Frowning slightly, she tilted her head back. "Seizures," she said quietly. "The gentleman's name is Martin, and he wears the helmet because when he goes down, he goes hard and fast. It saves his skull from being cracked wide open."

Dan swallowed. Shame hit him. Shame for his careless flippancy, for not understanding a damned thing. "I'm sorry." He swallowed again. "Like I said, I'm floundering with this."

"It's no wonder," Shelly repeated, "we can't be what you're used to."

"I thought I was being the knight gallant to the fair lady in the chair, and she was laughing her electric wheels off. I don't know if I can deal with all these surprises you promised me."

The song blasting from the loudspeakers blended into another. Shelly remained with Dan's arms around her, their feet barely shuffling across the polished wood floor. "Some people can't," she said simply.

Dan's interest sharpened at the softly resigned note in her voice. He didn't need to see her eyes to know her thoughts weren't solely focused on him. "Are you making comparisons? Now might be a good time to discuss the jerk this test was named after."

Even surrounded by dozens of gyrating bodies, he could feel her sudden tenseness. Under the blaring music and voices, he could hear the inhalation of a swift breath. She pulled back, but he had no intention of letting her get too far. A tense silence hung between them for a few moments before she finally answered. "Look, I don't owe you anything, least of all an explanation."

"That's right," he agreed, and waited.

A few more moments of silence trudged by. Then her conscience forced her to say, "I have been making comparisons. I'm sorry."

"Apology accepted," Dan said, nearly growling the words.

Finally, Shelly shrugged. Dan was a master at this holdout game. No doubt he'd had years of practice over a boardroom table. She could imagine people much stronger than herself squirming under such unrelenting patience.

"Nothing happened that you can't guess," she murmured a shade testily. "Spencer was a lot like you. Your backgrounds are similar—socially prominent families with high expectations. He wanted me to share his life, and I did for a while. But there were parts of my life he simply wouldn't—" she bit her lip "—or couldn't accept."

"Richard Robert?"

"Yes." Her gaze swept around the gymnasium floor, taking in the wheelchairs, crutches, artificial limbs and helmets, the imperfect bodies of the dancers, the smell of inexpensive cologne and the sweetness of spilled punch and crumbled sugar cookies. The sounds were equally out of sync: loud music; high-pitched laughter; slurred, often indecipherable speech. For the unindoctrinated, Shelly knew, it took time to see past the obvious. People could be so darned... skittish. And some, like Spencer, kept their eyes deliberately averted. "Yes," she said again, "Richard Robert, this part, all of it."

"But you accept it?"

"This is my world, Dan. I've known most of these people for years. Martin works alongside Richard Robert in a sheltered workshop. Corrie, the fair lady in the chair, has the same case manager."

"What about you, Shelly? All this is for your brother. What's left for you?"

"What's left is left," she said simply. "I watched my father kill himself with work so that he could provide a place and financial security for Richard Robert. Before he died, I promised Dad that I would always keep a space open in my life for Richard."

"Little martyr."

The growled accusation startled a soft bubble of laughter from her throat. "Not so." She met his heavy frown with a wide smile. "Where else can you go and not have to pay for this kind of fun." Stepping back, she glanced quickly around the dance floor and waved her hand. "Why, just look at Martin move—down and dirty, the sly old devil. And here comes Mavis. Do you know she's worn that same gown to the Christmas party every year since 1972? It's tradition. Dan, what is it?"

"Mavis?"

"Well, the dress has been cleaned since then."

"No, Mavis. I'd forgotten about her. Oh, Lord, don't tell me, is she coming this way?"

Confused, Shelly looked around Dan's shoulder to verify that Mavis was, indeed, walking toward them. Blankly, she looked back at Dan. "Yes."

"Don't look like that." He swallowed his own desperation. "It's not me. Why do you think I was hiding out in a dark corner, backside to the wall? She must have decided I was worth the denture cream. Twice she's asked me to dance and twice she..." Under the glitter of the revolving mirror ball, Dan's smooth, tanned face turned a dark, dull red. "It happened fast," he growled indignantly. "Under my jacket, around the waist and right for the behind. I'm telling you, Shelly, they were open-handed, full-palmed... gropes."

To her credit, Shelly did not laugh. One look into the glitter of his offended eyes told her it would be unwise to laugh. And after all, she decided charitably, how many dragons was one mortal prince supposed to conquer in a single day?

## *Chapter Nine*

The house was stone-cold. Outside, frigid wind blew away the lingering traces of last night's storm, and there were still two hours or so until morning. Dan left his vigil by the window, where he had been staring out at nothing but blank whiteness, and turned toward the bed.

Shelly Barker's bed.

Again he had offered to sleep on the couch. For the second night she had refused to let him, explaining that Richard Robert had a tendency to wander in the dark. If that happened, it would be best if she, rather than Dan, was on hand to deal with the situation. She'd also suggested, casually, that he lock the bedroom door. Or if he couldn't sleep in a closed room—some people couldn't—to keep his personal property within reach.

The bright little smile of hers as she had offered the advice was only one of the many things that had Dan pacing icy floors at four o'clock in the morning.

He had to wonder if insomnia was to be the natural order of things in his relationship with Shelly. Strange, he had never had that problem before.

Stranger still were the things that ran through a man's mind in the hours before dawn, when a soft, woman-scented bed only made him toss restlessly and ache. He could have eased the chill by covering his body with more than a brief pair of Jockey shorts, but the discomfort was nearly as effective as a cold shower. Better to pace with goose bumps on his butt as his bare feet wore tracks over the cold, wooden floor.

She would be needing the Christmas tree set up before he left. Dan had thought about doing it yesterday—*was it yesterday?*—when they had returned from shopping, but there hadn't been time. Not after having spent thirty-five minutes under the shower, scrubbing at sticky pine tar. Not without an electric drill to bore a hole for the stand. When he had asked if she had a drill, Shelly had given him a blank, speak-English look.

An incident from long ago surfaced on a forgotten page in his mind. Dan had presented a check at one of his mother's charity balls sponsoring the Special Olympics. To accept the check, an adorable young girl with Down's syndrome had been waiting on stage with him. When the presentation was over, the girl reached up, as prearranged for the camera, and kissed his cheek. Why had it never occurred to him that that charming, smiling child would grow older, but would never completely grow up. Like Richard Robert.

Dan hadn't given the girl or her family a second thought. How was he supposed to know about wheelchair brakes, football helmets and Mavis's hormones? Was ignorance an excuse or a reason?

Okay, so Shelly didn't own a drill. He would figure something else out. She had mentioned a toolbox somewhere in the room off the kitchen. Maybe he would take a look and, while he was at it, crank up the heat. The hard edge of his mouth tilted in a stiff, cold smile. Anything, he thought, to keep himself from thinking. And to keep him out of the bed. Her bed.

The scent of pinion pine drew him up the narrow, dark hall to the living room. His feet stopped at the entrance, and he took in the sight before him. As a distraction from the debacle of previous hours, the scene could not have been more effective.

This was what Dan was used to. This was familiar. A situation he could control. He did not see any wine or hear music, but Shelly had set a seductive stage. It pleased him that she had gone to so much trouble.

A fire burned brightly in the fireplace, casting flickering light throughout the shadowy room. His guilt over the much-contested couch changed to anticipation as he saw that it opened into a pillow-plumped, quilt-covered double bed. Shelly's pensive figure, knees drawn up, huddled back against the pillows. Her attention seemed to be absorbed by the scarlet-and-orange flames.

Remorse warred with tenderness. How long, Dan wondered, had she been waiting? She looked incredibly childlike, surrounded as she was by mounds of quilts and pillows. And she looked lonely, a somber study of shadow and light with the dancing fire as a backdrop. Dan looked on for a long moment, and the words came out of his mouth before he knew they were there.

"I'm cold, Shelly. Warm me."

At the sound of his voice, Shelly turned her head. The instant smile she gave him was as generous and unguarded as her gesture of folding back the quilts to offer the warm, waiting space beside her.

Walking forward, something clenched in the vicinity of Dan's chest. The feeling startled him, and he tried to identify it. He'd almost swear it was his heart pumping, beating overtime, but with more than desire. With Shelly it happened instantly, the logic of his mind giving over to emotion.

The heat under the quilts was a jolt to his chilled flesh as he slid in to sit beside her. "You were waiting for me."

"I was thinking about you," she countered, whispering. With a shy smile, she reached for his cold hands to chafe warmth back into them. "Does that count?"

By degrees, Dan's numbed body began to thaw. He half closed his eyes at the intensely pleasurable sensations her coddling created. "It counts," he growled when she moved to share her body heat, the soft weight of her surprisingly plump little breasts pushing against him.

He wondered if she had any idea of how warm was warm enough when she took his hands to slip them under her top and hold them to the bare flesh of her middle.

"Armpits work best," she murmured, "but this should do."

Yeah. Dan rolled his eyes. She was doing it, all right. Normally, it took him longer to reach this point of arousal, but then, so far, nothing about his relationship with Shelly Barker was normal. He cleared his throat. "What are you wearing?"

His question appeared to startle her, her slight body tensed. "Thermals, why?"

Dan closed his eyes on a long sigh. Since losing his virginity at sixteen, he had been met with sheer silk, starkly erotic teddies, G-strings and every form of seductive night attire in between. How, then, could the feel of waffled cotton and the clean, crisp fragrance of marmalade hair push his libido right off the Richter scale? He wondered what the family would say were it ever discovered that he, Dan Sutherland, had developed a fetish for baggy flannel, scratchy cotton and sliding socks.

"Dan?"

"Nothin', darlin'." An odd spasm of pain briefly twisted his features. "No reason for asking." Definitely time to change the subject. "You were thinking of me when I came in. You said you were."

"I was thinking of Corrie, too. She won't forget tonight, Dan, never. She'll always remember dancing with a real Prince Charming. Whatever test you think you took, I'd give you an *A*."

Her candor was as telling as the compulsive movement of her small body under his hands. "And I was thinking, if only. You know how the game goes? If only I had more nerve. If only you weren't *the* Dan Sutherland, but just you, the man. And I wondered if there ever would be a good time to stop feeling sorry for myself, walk up the hall to the bedroom and do my own negotiating." Her sigh was deep and slow. "The answer hadn't come to me yet."

The delicate flesh under his hands was soft as any wish and just as tempting. Closing his eyes, Dan extracted his hands from beneath her top and forced control to his escalated breathing. He took time and care to bank the pillows higher, enclose the covers more securely around them and settle her weight more comfortably against him. He could hear the uneven tremor in her breathing, sensed her restlessness in the pounding of her heart and by the heat of her skin. Her very stillness told Dan that the night's waiting had been as terrible for her as it had been for him.

"You know," he began slowly, "there is nothing a man enjoys more than getting plowed under by a steamroller. Hasn't anyone warned you what that kind of honesty does to the simple male mind?"

"Not you." Shelly was sure of it. "You were once described as a superman."

"Damn press."

The sound of his low growl rumbled in her ear. Somehow, her arm had come to be draped across his middle, and her hand rested low at the lean curve of his waist. The fabric of his Jockey shorts was the only barrier between her curious fingers and the shape and texture of his hipbone. Her breasts pressed intimately against his side, and with his arm around her shoulders, her cheek lie on the hard, muscled wall of his chest.

The light from the fire flickered and swayed, snapped and danced. Wherever they touched brought Shelly trembling pleasure. She hoped he wouldn't begrudge her a small taste, because even with a fierce mental lecture on self-control, there was no way she could *not* do what she did next. Impulsively, helplessly, she turned her face and brushed her open mouth against him.

Tasting satin skin, tasting smooth muscle over bone, she savored his exotic tang and salty flavor. She breathed in the basic smell that was part soap and cologne, part the unique musk of aroused male. She heard the altered thud of his heart under her cheek and felt the shivers of his flesh under the damp glide of her mouth.

She only meant to sample, but every nerve in her whole body coiled with an excitement that bordered on terror. It wasn't fair of him to push his way into her life and make her feel this way, feverish and raw, empty and wanting. She'd been just fine without him. The injustice of his Sutherland arrogance filled her with a sudden angry impotence, and she sank her teeth into his shoulder with an almost savage delicacy.

Dan's head fell back against the bank of pillows even as a shudder shook his big body. "Like I said . . . as lethal as a steamroller." He took her hand and drew it to his mouth to kiss the open palm, then forced a grin to hide the utter seriousness of his question. "More?"

Her trembling sigh brushed his neck like the glide of warm, golden light. "This isn't real. It isn't helping."

"It isn't hurting."

Shelly made a tiny sound of pleading. "Yes, it is . . . me. You are everything I swore I would never do again. It scares me how fast this is happening. Dan, we're strangers."

"No, darlin'," he murmured, "not since you dragged those pennies out of your pocket and paid for my coffee. I recognized you, Shelly."

Brushing her cheek along his shoulder, she tilted her head and met his sober gaze with her own. "You couldn't have."

"Oh, yes," he taunted, amused as much by his own conviction as her skepticism. "Remind me to tell you about it sometime."

Now was the time to give her gentle words and reassurance. He wanted Shelly to have them. Of all the women he had ever known, she deserved them. Bending his head, Dan meant to drop a kiss on her nose, but strangely, her mouth was closer. He saw the change in her face just before his eyelids dropped and the light, reassuring kiss he'd meant to give altered in its intent and focus, became an act of mating.

He felt the surprised, shivery tremble of her body just before their breathing merged and shuddered between them. He tasted her fully and, impatient with the barriers, lifted her higher, pushing aside the cotton of her top so that under the covers, her bare breasts brushed, then flattened against his chest. Shelly's breath caught on a gasp as she threw back her head, her body fitting to his.

Through the pads of his fingers, Dan could feel the jangle of nerves under her soft skin, the swift and erratic pulse of blood through her veins. He'd never known a woman so lacking in pretence. Everything she felt was open to him—the arch of her hips against his thigh, the needy sounds she made in her throat, the fog of pleasure in her half-closed eyes.

He was desperate enough that he trembled like a boy. Yet, he, a man who had never had to wait or cherish, forced himself to slow and to savor. His plan wasn't to take Shelly in that kind of hotheaded frenzy. Not the first time.

Taking her hand, he brushed a kiss over the delicate knuckles and placed the palm flat against the hard drum of his heart. "Now try and tell me we're strangers."

It took a moment. At first he was unaware of the tentative, hold-off pressure of her small hand against the swift rise and fall of his chest. He did not understand or want to acknowledge the hesitation he saw in her eyes. His own hand, the one holding her against him, eased its pressure, but did not let go. Instead it moved upward, the fingers curling around her neck under the silky weight of her hair.

"Too fast? We can slow it down."

Shelly drew away just enough to meet his eyes. "We can't. We have to stop."

Pushing back the heavy skein of hair that had fallen to cover her face and muffle her words, he asked simply, "Why?"

"Because it's getting out of hand." She knew it was time to stop, but as she pushed away, the hand resting on his chest slipped. In an instant, the offending member skidded downward, over his belly to his lap.

The muscled wall of his abdomen sucked inward even as his hips jerked, and the hard ridge of his arousal leapt eagerly toward the inadvertent pressure of her hand. Any intelligent thought she might have had left vanished in that dazzling heartbeat of surprise. She felt as if she were a young innocent again. Felt, in touching Dan Sutherland, as if she'd just discovered the essence and power of man. She experienced the same thrill of awe and fear.

For a second, unthinking of the consequences, her fingers closed around him through the fabric of his shorts. It took but a moment to learn his hardness, to trace his length. Impressions rushed to her brain. Sensations of heat and strength, of promise and pleasure.

Dan's reaction was a sharp, indrawn breath. "Shelly!"

A long sigh seemed to shake her entire body, and she held him compulsively for one last, sweet moment before reluctantly drawing away.

Forcing herself to look toward the fire, Shelly searched for the strength—or will—to sit independently. Pushing back against the pillows, she drew her knees to her chest, wrapped her arms around her legs instead of around Dan and dropped her head in what appeared to be defeat.

"Did I mention I was waiting for a better time than this?"

While his own body urged him to seek more of her sweet, warm touches, there was part of his mind left with enough sense to recognize pain in the quiet, muffled words. Soothingly, Dan brushed his hand over the crown of her bright hair, over her shoulders and down her slender spine. "What is it, darlin'? What's wrong?"

The effort to lift her head was great. Shelly's pale blue eyes echoed the regret and resignation in her forced smile. "Timing." She shook the hair back from her face and touched his arm. "It's all in the timing." Her voice was thin as tissue. "We're not alone."

Dan stared at the small, competent hand on his arm. His blank gaze swung around the quiet room, penetrating shadows and examining corners. Slowly, so slowly, his gaze wandered back to the bulky pile of quilts on the far side of the bed and then to Shelly. Another sluggish minute droned by as he assessed the near-helpless apology in her eyes. "You weren't waiting for me." It was a flat statement.

"I was thinking about you, though."

He should have known that his fantasy of Shelly, warm and waiting by the fire, had been too good to be true. If his brains hadn't already been in his shorts with his first step up the hall, he probably would have figured it out sooner. Hell, a Sutherland was nothing if not perceptive.

"Richard Robert."

Dan opened his mouth, paused, and closed it. "Why isn't your brother in his own bed?"

"Because I have to monitor the heating pad."

"Oh." Dan thought it over carefully, "I see."

"Richard Robert overextended himself today," she explained quietly. "I knew he would, and I knew he wouldn't be able to sleep once the pain started. Arthritis, in his hips and down through his legs." She shook her hair back from her face. "Too much dancing and tramping through the snow looking for just the right tree. Anyway, heat, aspirin and quiet seem to help. I have him in here because it's easier to monitor the heating pad. If he's lucky, he can ride it out and sleep through the worst of it."

"If he's not so lucky?"

Shelly turned her head to give Dan a direct, level look. "Then I wait it out with him."

For the first time Dan noticed the faint shadows under her eyes and the fine tremor in her smile. "How long have you been at this?" he asked quietly, and the gentleness of his voice masked his growing anger. All right, so he was an arrogant ass, but didn't she need a keeper?

"Oh." Her narrow shoulders moved fretfully, "Awhile."

He wondered how she measured time. Did "awhile" mean minutes? An hour? Or did "awhile" mean ever since they'd returned from the party some six hours ago? Dan was torn between the desire to snatch her up and protect her from what he was beginning to see as an obsessive martyr complex and the need to grab hold and shake it out of her.

In the end he did neither. Instead he simply asked, "What can I do to help?"

A dozen different emotions flashed across her startled expression. Amazement was one. He had to be as physically frustrated as she. She'd felt his heat and hardness, caressed it, wanted it. Then came wonder. His smile was strained, but it was still a smile when he had every right to feel cheated and angry. She should have mentioned Richard Robert's presence the minute Dan had stepped into the room. The least she'd owed him was fair warning. But she hadn't. Not when the sight of his beautiful, seminude body in the firelight had taken the last thought from her head and breath from her lungs. No, she hadn't wanted Dan to turn back. She'd crossed her fingers and *willed* him forward.

The last emotion she felt was gratitude, and she gave a tired sigh imbued with it. "I'd love to take a break," she murmured wearily. "If you could just watch that he stays put, even if he wakes up. I'll be quick and—"

"Shelly...go."

After meticulously counting the ceiling tiles and estimating the square footage of pine paneling on the walls, Dan got up to add another log to the fire. With Shelly taking her time in the back of the house, his attention focused on Richard Robert. Being careful not to disturb the sleeping man, Dan approached the quilts and reached for the top layer of covers.

The crackling fire threw off an orange glow. At the disturbance, glazed blue eyes blinked, then opened fully. Richard Robert lay unmoving, staring back without any trace of his normal curiosity or interest brightening his gaze. His skin was translucent pale, and the flush that mantled his cheeks stood out with rash-pink vividness.

As had happened frequently during the past few days, Dan found himself at a loss. He swallowed heavily. This was no Richy trick. The blue eyes staring up at him were near real tears. Feeling helpless, Dan patted pockets in jeans he wasn't wearing, looked for clues in the fire, for directions written on the walls. What did one do? What kind of comfort was offered to a hurting man-child.

"Hey, pal." He reached out and moved a strand of hair away from the listless blue gaze. "Rough time?"

Shelly, shadowed and silent in the darkened hall, stood perfectly still. Her throat ached with swallowed emotion. Not once, not ever, could she remember Spencer reaching out to touch her brother.

The last thing she'd wanted to do was get involved with Dan Sutherland, but after tonight, she would never regret that she had known him.

On bare, silent feet, she stepped into the room. "He can't hear you."

A smile came to Richard Robert the moment his sister walked into view. Dan was caught, fascinated by it. "I didn't notice before." His own smile was lopsided. "But he looks a lot like you, Shelly. Especially when he's pleased... the same clean, delicate bone structure and electric smile. It's too bad he's—" Dan held back the rest of the thought. What was, was. "He's a good-looking kid."

"Hmm," Shelly agreed as she sat the tray down. From the various items on it, she selected a glass of water and an aspirin tablet. "In his other life, he's a real heartbreaker."

As Dan looked on, Richard Robert pulled himself to a sitting position, signed a comment to his sister and began a careful examination of the medication she offered.

"His other life?"

"Yes, his other one." She smiled absently, keeping her eyes fixed on Richard Robert until he swallowed the tablet. "The one where everyone appreciates his practical jokes, where his curiosity is channeled into a brilliant career of, say, scientific research. Where—" She stood back and signed a response to a question. "He's feeling better. He wants to watch TV."

"A good sign?"

"Always. He may be down, but he isn't out." Shelly left the room for a moment and returned with the remote control unit for the television. After putting the unit into her brother's hands, she turned to Dan, motioning toward the tray. "I've brought enough tea to share. Or would you rather go back to bed, try and sleep?"

Dan knew nothing had changed back in that cold, woman-scented torture chamber. He looked at the tray, then at Richard Robert. This had not been the weekend he had envisioned as he'd stormed up the hill, but there were, he was coming to realize, some situations in which a man had to take what was offered.

Compromise was needed for them all to get settled under the quilts; Shelly again in the middle, Dan to the right, Richard Robert to the left. Richard Robert took his time, holding the remote-control box like a loaded revolver as he shot slowly through every channel on network and cable. When he finally found what he was looking for, he settled contentedly against his nest of pillows, pushing against his sister's shoulder.

"Shelly?" Dan forced the growl out of his voice. The Sutherlands did not nor had they ever ground their teeth. "Even at this hour, there must be something better to watch."

"Sorry," she murmured, and yawned. She nestled against Dan's shoulder, unwittingly subjecting him to the scent of her hair and the soft crush of her breasts as she inched over for Richard Robert.

"The thing is, most of the old movies are strong on dramatic dialogue and mood music. Not much to them if you can't hear what's going on. Now this channel? Where else can you see neck veins bulging, book waving and fist pounding? We don't need volume to know this man is excited."

Shelly fell asleep within fifteen minutes. Dan suffered through every minute of his hour of destiny. This was not, he decided with wry irony, how he had envisioned their first night in bed together.

The tick of the clock in the kitchen proclaimed the coming dawn. Only once did he permit himself a glance across Shelly's slumbering form to glower malevolently at the sublimely enrapt Richard Robert.

## *Chapter Ten*

"Dan, I'm sorry, but do you need to wake up? Richy, that was definitely a growl...I'm telling you for the last time, leave him alone."

Dan sifted through the webs of consciousness. He didn't want to, but the layers shredded around him, and he was left with no choice but to join the living. Swearing slightly, he pressed the heels of his hands against his eyes to rub out the grit. Then he dragged himself back against the pillows, feeling the weight on his legs as he blinked groggily.

His brain refused to process the information his eyes were receiving. Blinking again, he looked farther around the room. That had been Shelly's voice he'd heard, but where was her soft hand to soothe his brow?

All he could see was a mop of a dark, mussed hair and a pair of determined eyes staring at him from the bottom of the bed. Dan would have said he was immune to any more surprises, but waking up to find Richard Robert with a half nelson around his ankles was a bit much, even after last night.

"Shelly?"

"Here..." her voice was softly hesitant.

Dan dragged himself higher, taking Richard Robert with him. "Where?"

"Behind you." She stepped into view, running her hands nervously down the sides of her pleated gray trousers.

Dan's voice was gruffly neutral. "What, ah, what time is it?"

Shelly's gaze bounced off Richard Robert, and she looked down quickly to examine her left thumb. "It's after ten—not late, but getting there. I didn't know what time you had to leave."

"My flight leaves at one."

"Oh." She nodded.

"Shelly?"

Seeing no other way, she slowly walked to the foot of the bed and stopped. Dan's bare chest and shoulders were flushed from sleep, and she heard the rasp of his hand as he rubbed it against his early-morning beard. He looked big, blurry eyed and capable of much more than a surly growl now that he was awake. He'd lost his easy smile in the wee hours of the morning, and it appeared his tolerance was next.

"I guess you're wondering...?" She drew in a breath, and her gaze followed Dan's to her brother wrapped around his feet at the bottom of the bed.

"Is this another one of those dragons you warned me about?" Dan asked cautiously, flexing his legs. Richard Robert tightened his hold on Dan's ankles, but made no other move.

Shelly's head tipped consideringly. "I'm not sure. He's had you like that for a while now. I think if he was going to...if he was going to do something, he'd have done it while you were sleeping. It seems to me that he's fascinated with your ankles, or maybe it's your feet. He's been staring awfully hard at the hair on your big toes. I told you he's curious about everything."

"What," Dan asked carefully, "would you suggest I do now?"

She paused for a moment. "I don't know." She shrugged. "He's never done anything like this before."

There was nothing amused in the curl of Dan's mouth. "Not even with what's-his-name . . . Spencer, wasn't it?"

"Spencer's method of dealing with Richard Robert was to ignore him totally."

"I don't think," Dan gritted out slowly, "that will work right now."

Shelly turned her head to look at him and bit her lip. "As a method, it never was effective," she said quietly, then hesitated. "You could always ask Richy to explain himself."

"I'm not sure I want to know." Dan tried moving just his left leg this time, but it remained secured along with his right. "And I don't speak the language, remember?"

"We're going to have to do something. I've tried talking to him, reasoning, everything short of physically prying him loose while you were asleep."

"Well, darlin', it's a fact I can't take him back to Denver with me."

Shelly found herself wincing at the silky sarcasm she heard in Dan's voice. This might be easier, she decided, if he'd simply roar and get it over with. Well—she tried to shrug philosophically—she had promised him a memorable weekend, but enough was enough. After this stunt of Richard Robert's, there was no further point to prove. With less than four hours of sleep behind him and Richard Robert locked around his legs, Dan appeared to be a man who had been pushed to the limit.

Kneeling, she tipped her brother's chin up so that he was forced to look at her. In sign, she asked again what he was doing. He'd refused to before, but this time Richard Robert gave her an answer.

"Well?" Dan prodded, irritated with himself because he couldn't understand the swift flashing of hands. "What is this all about?"

With a hand on her brother's shoulder, Shelly steadied herself as she rose to her feet. She didn't answer immediately, and when she did, her voice was small and tight. "He's holding on to you...so that you can't take me away."

Past mistakes, she realized numbly, could rear up and literally steal a woman's breath from her body. Guilt when mixed with bitter shame could destroy a spirit. The weight of those emotions had grown lighter over the past two years, but she doubted she'd ever be completely free. There was nothing anyone could think of her that was worse than she sometimes thought of herself, and Dan deserved an explanation.

"I've told you about Spencer." Her voice was emotionless. "But to understand Richard Robert's actions, I have to tell you my part." With a tender hand, she reached out to stroke her brother's dark hair away from his eyes.

"Spencer was very open with his objections about Richard Robert, and very persuasive." Her eyes closed as she remembered just how persuasive he had been, and she swallowed, remembering, also, how easily she'd let herself be persuaded.

"There was a time I quit thinking for myself," she continued, neither minimizing nor inflating her part. "Because it was so important to Spencer, I disassociated myself from my brother. I took Richard Robert from his own home and put him with strangers. There was a year—nearly a whole damned year—where I ignored his existence."

She swallowed past the constriction in her throat. What she'd done was unforgivable, and the hollow ache of regret was never far away. "Richard only knows that because of a man, his entire life changed. I left him and didn't come back. In his own way, he's trying to stop it from happening again."

"So what happened?" Dan couldn't prevent the harshness in his voice. She was beating herself with a heavy stick, when most of the flogging belonged to a jerk named Spencer. "Did he bail out of the marriage, or did you?"

Shelly blinked, drawn back from the painful memory. "Marriage?" she repeated blankly. "Did I give you that impression?" She gave him a bright, empty smile. "Marriage was never an issue, at least not in his mind."

Her eyes held a bewildered, unfocused look. Even now, she couldn't understand how she'd been so blind so long.

"You see, Spencer couldn't take the chance that the 2.3 children he planned to have in his perfect life would be less than—" her gaze darted to Richard Robert "—perfect. So after nearly a year together, one day he announced that he'd met a woman with an impeccable genetic history, a family as socially prominent as his own and a biological clock that was ticking. They were married eight weeks later."

With a visible shake, she bent down and signed something to her brother. It took him a moment to respond, but when he did, he freed his captive and, with a grin, leapt from the bed.

Dan called to Shelly before she, too, could escape into another room. "What did you tell him?"

"Only the obvious." That bright, empty smile came again. "That if he didn't let go, you wouldn't be able to leave."

"Shelly," Dan called softly, "this conversation isn't finished. Don't walk away."

Her voice was quiet and steady. "Hasn't it occurred to you yet that I can't walk away, not ever again." She threw up her hands in an encompassing gesture. "It doesn't get better than this. Richard Robert isn't a child who's going to grow up and stop needing me. I'm here...for the duration."

Twenty minutes later, showered and partially dressed, the smell of coffee lured Dan back down the hall, and he stood, slouched against the doorjamb, watching Shelly Barker. There was something almost too determined in the way she moved around the kitchen, furiously stirring something in a bowl when an electric mixer would have been easier. When she began smashing halved oranges into an old-fashioned glass juicer, he decided it was time to announce himself.

"Need some help?"

"Oh!" Shelly whirled around and a pulpy mass of orange rind flew from her hand to skid across the counter.

Dan crossed the room, taking a cloth from the sink to mop up the sticky mess. "Sorry about that. You were concentrating pretty hard. You do have a thing about breakfast, don't you?"

"No—" She started to make a denial, then gave him her first uncomplicated grin of the morning. "Yes, but don't ask me to explain. I've discovered that when food has to be done before noon, it's best just to get it over with."

"Shelly, you don't have to do this for me."

"I don't mind." She waved her hand and laughed at his skeptical frown. "No, honestly. I enjoy cooking, I do...just not consuming what I cook before my stomach settles for the day."

She gave him another smile and turned to the task at hand, which was making the most elegant brunch she could manage because *something* had to go right before he left. If a meal was all she could give Dan after this sorry excuse for a weekend, she'd fight her ridiculous queasiness, cranky ovens and yellow egg slime to give it.

After spilling her miserable little story, she had decided that Dan's last impression of the Barkers would not be one of unending chaos and cartoon melodrama. If nothing else, she wanted the last hour he spent on her hill to be normal.

"Your job might be easier if you had a few modern gadgets in here." He'd been watching her methodically smash and twist the last of the orange halves into juice; guaranteed to be fresh, but a strain on a slender arm. "Aren't there appliances to do this sort of thing?"

Shelly stopped, midtwist and pushed the hair away from her face with the back of her hand. "There are gadgets for everything." She sighed wistfully, flexing her cramped, sticky fingers.

With his hip against the cabinet, Dan folded his arms across his chest and took a look around the room. "How does Richard Robert feel about not living with you anymore?"

It was difficult to tell if he was asking because he genuinely wanted to know or if he was merely making polite conversation. She shrugged, deciding to take his question at face value.

"He was at an age, anyway, where he needed more supervision than I could give him. Not that he was ever aggressively uncontrollable," she hastened to explain, "but he had some definite personality quirks. As my business grew more demanding, I couldn't give him the time and attention he needed. Plus, now that he's in the system, he gets a lot of one-on-one training in living skills that he couldn't get with just me."

Dan's gaze sporadically roamed the room. Now that it was nearly time to leave, he found himself wondering how to go on. And, he was forced to admit, he was unsure where he even wanted to go.

Once more he found himself reaching for a neutral subject. "When do you take him back to his group home?"

Shelly was amazed, honestly stunned, at how much it hurt that he had to search for polite conversation. The only thing worse would be a friendly handshake as he bid her goodbye on his way out the door. Still, she couldn't blame him. It had to be difficult on a man's ego to storm a hill and then have to backpedal like hell to get off it.

Lecturing herself on the futility of wishes, she forced a smile and an easy answer. "Early this afternoon. I have to get him back so that he's organized for work on Monday. Smells like the sweet rolls are warmed through. I hope you like them with your coffee." She made the mistake of looking at him, and the strain of the last forty hours shifted and resettled.

He was so much more than she'd imagined he would be. A generous man and a sensitive one. She had never expected to feel anything like this again, the hope and longing, the resurgence of wishes and dreams. Last night had been the first time in a long while that she'd played her if-only game. If only she had more of whatever intrinsic ingredient other women seemed to possess, a unique something that made them lovable and desirable, warts and all. Or lacking that, if only the threads of love and responsibility binding her to this hill weren't quite so daunting.

She lowered her eyes, then her head, but Dan's image stayed with her. His stance was loose and easy, yet even relaxed, there was authority in the tilt of his head, strength in character as well as the flesh. She almost wished that *he* was less. If only there was less warmth in his clear brown eyes, or perhaps less grace and power of body and mind. If only his hands weren't quite so hard and strong, his fingers as sensitive or his touch innately delicate. How much less shattering, then, to watch him go.

Above her head, his sigh reminded her of where she was, what she was and what she had to do. She gathered her smile and the threads of the inane chatter she'd been bombarding him with.

"They're homemade, the sweet rolls. I binge bake and then freeze. If you'd like to pour yourself a cup of coffee, I'll call Richard Robert."

All she wanted now was to get through to the end with as much dignity—and normalcy—as possible.

Coming to a dead stop at the threshold of the living room, Shelly groaned, kissing her faint hope goodbye. She knew in an instant that the room was out of kilter, but it took a few moments to grasp the magnitude.

Shelly was a modern woman, but it took a cautious step and closer examination, before she was ready to believe the suspicions in her mind. With a sinking heart, she weakly reached for the support of the nearest chair. Maybe, she thought as she collapsed into it, she didn't see what she thought she saw.

While she had been in the kitchen, her brother had been setting the stage for his own version of a farewell party. He stood by the now cold fireplace, ba-humming excitedly as he pointed out his handiwork. In one hand he held a roll of masking tape and a mangled tail of crepe paper. In the other, he tightly clutched the last of some "balloons."

"What have you done?"

She didn't sign because she didn't expect an answer, nor was one necessary. Although she recognized the crepe paper from a long-forgotten birthday celebration, Richy had not found his foil-wrapped party "balloons" in her bedside drawer. Which meant that the only other way he could have found these decorations was by riffling through their houseguest's personal belongings. Damn it, she'd warned Dan to keep his things locked up.

"Shelly?" A call came from the kitchen. "Do you want these rolls out of the oven?"

Her eyes popped open as she sprang from the chair. She wasn't about to sit around and wait for doom to descend. These two days were going to end with dignity. Richy's party was over. "Yes," she called back, "take them out."

Frantically, she snatched at the nearest piece of evidence, but Richard Robert had done a formidable job of taping the thing to the wooden mantle, and even with both hands, it slipped through her fingers, bobbing back against the brick facing then diving to the left. For a startled instant she stared at the faint, glistening residue on her hands.

Her stomach lurched with horrified queasiness. Lubricated! How had Richard Robert managed to inflate all eight without gagging? The thought defied civilized comprehension.

Ignoring Richard Robert's ba-hum of outrage, she set her teeth and reached for the decoration again. This time she used more strength and what there was left of her fingernails. The thin latex gave way, exploding with a dull pop. One down, she eyed the others grimly, seven to go.

"Is this a family game?" Dan asked politely. He stood at the edge of the room, an amused, puzzled expression crinkling his eyes, hesitantly pulling at the corner of his mouth. He hadn't figured it out yet. "Or can anyone play?"

He would.

When the last round was over, a woman could either admit defeat or tilt her chin and leave the ring in style. Tossing the scraps into the fireplace, Shelly lifted her chin.

"Richard Robert decided to throw you a going-away party."

"Did he now?" Dan stepped into the room.

Shelly moved closer to her brother. "Of course, everyone knows you have to have decorations for a party."

"Hmm."

"And since there was nothing but crepe paper in the house—" she swallowed "—he apparently went through your things for the... rest. I mentioned—didn't I mention?—that you should keep your personal things locked up."

Her eyes were wide and wary as Dan stopped. His puzzled expression slowly changed to one of comprehension. Color, a deep, dark tide of red, crept from the open collar of his shirt, up his neck and into his face. Several times his mouth opened, but no distinguishable sound came out.

"The other night...Friday night, when I asked what your plans were," she reminded him with a bright smile, humor, the only defense left, glimmering in her innocent gaze, "you told me you hadn't made any definite plans beyond getting here."

With thumb and forefinger, she flicked at one of the seven remaining condoms taped and bobbing across the mantel of her fireplace. The flick sent the one bouncing against its neighbors, to set them all aweave, like airy dominos.

"This kind of party doesn't work with used props." She looked guilelessly into his eyes. "So it's probably just as well you didn't have anything specific in mind."

Shelly forced herself to chew and then swallow a mouthful of tasteless food. The only person unaware of the claustrophobic atmosphere around the table was Richard Robert, ba-humming his way through a second sweet roll. She tried to remember a time in her life more miserable than this one and decided that she would willingly live through Spencer's surprise wedding announcement again, if only Dan would say something.

She could feel the shimmer of his fury. He was no more interested in this meal than she was, but because she had prepared it, civility dictated that he remain to eat it. If this wasn't her house, *she* would have gotten up and left.

Okay, so he had a right to be angry. His privacy had been invaded, his dignity dumped on and his ego trampled. If he'd just let go, instead of sitting there like a smoldering specter of outraged wrath, she'd apologize and get the damned thing over and done with.

"That was good, but I have to go." Dan's voice was as stiffly formal as his movements. Carefully, he wiped his mouth with a paper napkin and pushed his chair back.

Remaining at the table with Richard Robert, Shelly listened to the hollow ring of his footsteps as he moved through the rooms. The sound was quick and impatient on the hardwood floors. It was the sound of a man who had satisfied social protocol and now meant to make a quick getaway.

It would have been easier for her to rise and pace away the tension. Now, she thought, would have been a good time to start nibbling on that hangnail. Unfortunately the thing was gone—she'd used it earlier as Dan slept and Richy clung. Since she'd never been a teeth gnasher or a hair twirler, the only thing she could do was sit up straight and wait.

There was, she knew, one last piece of propriety to be gotten through. Dan was too well-bred to simply leave. He would not take the easy, painless way and storm out. Natural courtesy would force him to stop long enough to say goodbye.

As if the thought had conjured the image, he stood in the doorway. In one hand he held the strap of his travel bag, and his coat was draped over his arm. He seemed to be on the verge of saying something, but for the life of her, she didn't know what else was left for either of them to say.

"I have to go now."

So what if he couldn't bring himself to meet her eyes, Shelly thought miserably. Did she really want to read what was in them? Sliding her hands off the table, Shelly brought them tightly together in her lap. "Would you like me to walk you to—"

"Don't bother. I'll see myself out."

She wouldn't cry. She would not let herself regret anything that had happened this weekend, although she did regret that Dan was leaving in a state of stiff, silent anger. Drawing in a deep breath, she could speak, but a smile was beyond her. "Well, then, drive carefully. The hill is bound to be icy."

Over Richard Robert's quiet hum, Shelly busied herself with clearing away the dishes. The dull slam of a car door sounded faintly through the frozen silence, and her fingers stilled as she listened for the start-up growl of the engine.

Forcing herself to function, she waited for that last sound. She wrapped and stored the leftovers, ran water in the sink. She watched the second hand on the wall clock sweep around and around the clock's face. Seventeen teeth-grinding sweeps later, she was still waiting.

Nerves were causing her hands to shake. Why, she wanted to scream, didn't he start the damned car? Maybe he couldn't. The thought crashed into her mind. Maybe, he'd thrown his bag into the passenger side of the car, slammed the door and in his anger he hadn't watched where he was going. That was it, of course. In his irate stalk to the driver's side, Dan had somehow managed to slip on the ice. While she cowered in the kitchen, he was outside in her driveway, bleeding and broken.

In a panicky rush, she veered off to her bedroom before slamming back to the kitchen, instructing Richard Robert to stay in the house. In her mind she saw the gruesome scene. It had to be Dan's head; not a broken leg at all...or maybe both. In his fall he must have dashed his skull against the side of the car, snapped his leg and, oh, God, probably an arm...and she'd let him lay there for seventeen minutes. Dan was dead, and the Barkers had killed him.

Just beyond the winter skeleton of the Russian olive trees, she came to a slamming halt. He was alive. The relief was dizzying, draining the blood from her head and the strength from her limbs. She floundered in the snow and righted, orienting more than her physical self.

Dan was in the car, simply sitting there watching her as she, catching her breath, looked back at him. Slowly, he leaned across the seat and opened the passenger door.

A glance over her shoulder assured Shelly that Richard Robert was still safely tucked inside the house. She approached the car cautiously, slipped in and closed the door.

As the cold invaded and the silence between them drew out, she found her gaze following Dan's to the end of the road and beyond, off into the bank of trees. What, she wondered, was so interesting about those trees that he would sit in a deathly cold car for nearly twenty minutes to watch them? He had a plane to catch, didn't he? Why didn't he turn the heater on? What was he still doing here?

It was as frigid inside the car as it was outside. When she could no longer stand the suspense, she cleared her throat, and said carefully, "It takes at least twenty-five minutes to get to the airport from here."

Dan made a noncommittal sound, and his voice was as neutral as hers had been. "Twenty-five minutes in your car." His glance swept to the four-wheel-drive vehicle sheltered under the carport. "Fifteen in this one."

Shelly looked at her hands and wondered how much time she had left before her nose started dripping. She looked out the window and then back at her hands. She sniffed. "I guess you'll be wanting to go soon . . . to get there on time, I mean."

Dan didn't move. His face was stiff and red with cold. He turned his head briefly to look at her, and she noticed his gaze slide away once before meeting her own.

"Well..." She tried for brightness, but the word came out brittle and forced. "Goodbye, again." Her gloved hand inched over the armrest, searching for a handle or latch that would open the door. "Drive carefully."

"Shelly?"

Dan's voice was quiet, a tone stretched thin with patience and the tiniest thread of...resignation? The sound of her name, said in just that manner stilled her hand. "Yes?"

"I'm not leaving."

He wasn't making a great deal of sense. All evidence pointed toward a leavetaking. The man had just endured a weekend no mortal man should have to. He was *sitting* in the car with the keys in the ignition. His travel bag was in the back seat and his hands were locked in bloodless blue fists around the steering wheel.

Because she didn't know what else to do, she turned her gaze back to the aspen trees. "Are you camping out here then?"

"It wasn't my original intention." His voice cracked, and his breath blew in hoary puffs between teeth that were clenched against the cold. "But when I got in the car—" he bunched his rigid shoulders "—I changed my mind."

Startled, she looked at him. "Why?"

"Because I've had a chance to think the situation through." He turned his head away, muttering, "When I stopped and thought about it, I realized that I was doing exactly what you said I would . . . double timing my dignity-shredded butt off your hill. How is that for predictable?"

"I thought you were disgusted."

"That, too." There was the faintest touch of humor in his mumble. "Disgusted with myself for letting a man less than half my size and mental weight confound me with my own ego. I thought I was better than that."

"Then you were angry?"

"For a few minutes I was," he said quietly. "But anger didn't drive me out of your house." His eyes were solemn and direct. "I left in an enraged huff because I was embarrassed...more than I've ever been. Walking into that room and seeing those condoms was like getting caught on stage with my pants down. I stormed out because I didn't know how to handle the feeling. All I could think of was getting out."

Shelly let out a shaky breath and almost laughed. A few minutes ago, she'd have sworn there was no humor left to be found. "This morning," she said, sinking deeper into the plush seat, closing her eyes and sighing heavily, "has been hideous."

"Lord, yes." Dan dropped his head back against the headrest. "I'll know better next time. Now that I've met the dragons, I'll leave the sword home and bring the Uzi."

She wanted to be strong and tell him that he did not have to use glib phrases or superficial words. She wanted to tell him that she was all right and would continue to be, even after he left. Don't promise, she wanted to plead, don't sound like you mean it and use words like "next time."

"I know you don't believe me." His voice quietly broke, and his words echoed the chain of her thoughts. "Not after this stunt. But you will."

Taking a deep, frosty breath, he tightened his grip on the wheel. "Which brings us to the final reason why I'm still parked on your hill."

Dan inhaled, then exhaled a cloud of icy vapor. "Yesterday when the auto club came to pull me out of the ditch, they must have left something on inside the car." His voice lowered to an even deeper level, just short of grating. "The damned battery is dead."

## *Chapter Eleven*

Shelly swallowed and the sound of her smothered gasp was audible in the stunned silence. She felt a second swelling in her chest and quickly looked away.

"You wouldn't think of laughing, would you?" Dan asked carefully. "After what I've been through, it would be rude of you to laugh."

Shelly bowed her head. "I'm sorry."

"You *do* find this amusing."

"No!" She held up a hand to ward off the accusation and bravely looked him in the face to convince him of her sincerity.

The last thing she expected was that his arm would come around her, gathering her close to his side. Or that the rumble of his laughter would liberate her own. Their voices blended in harmony to warm the frigid recesses of the car.

"After everything else, every... rotten... thing... else—" impulsively, Shelly leaned up and touched her mouth to his stiff cheek "—you weren't even allowed a dignified getaway."

Then a deep shudder shook her, and she made a small, helpless click in the back of her throat. She gave him a darting glance and just as quickly looked away.

Finally she said, "You might want to come back into the house where it's warm...." She hesitated and gave him another swift, appraising glance. "Because my jumper cables are in the back of Richard Robert's group-home van... across the valley and far, far away."

Dan opened his mouth. "I knew that." His chest rose and fell on a long, gusty sigh. "Of course, I knew that."

Walking ahead, she went quickly into the house, trying for diplomacy as Dan followed her through and picked up the phone in the kitchen. Shaking herself, she shed coat and gloves and walked down the hall to check on Richard Robert in his bedroom, then walked back up the hall.

"It's going to take the auto club fifty minutes to get here," Dan said as she entered the kitchen. He stood with one shoulder propping up the wall and one perfectly arched eyebrow cocked lopsidedly as he glared accusingly at the phone in his hand.

"It would take at least that long to drive down and get the jumper cables. I'd take you, but with your car blocking the driveway, I can't get out, either." She said nothing for a moment. "This means you'll have to rearrange your flight. Will there be another one out today, do you think?"

"One way to find out." Dan suddenly lifted his head to sniff. "Coffee... there's coffee left?" Judging by the hope in his voice, even dregs would do, as long as they were hot.

Once Dan had his cold fingers wrapped around a thick ceramic mug, Shelly continued on into the living room to straighten pillows and finish clearing away the farewell-party debris. Richard Robert scurried in after her and amused, she watched his exaggerated maneuvers, his scrupulous avoidance of the tall man in the kitchen. From the way he was behaving, one would have thought that Dan had done Richard Robert hours of grave injustice, not the other way around.

"Shelly?"

Why should the sound of her name fill her with apprehension? The pillow she held was punched and punched again. She dropped it back to the couch only to discover her hands were then empty. Turning toward him, her steps dragged and her senses strained to read the odd questioning inflection in Dan's voice as he called to her. What now? she wondered.

"I can reschedule the flight for tonight at seven, or—" he held his palm over the mouthpiece, watching, speaking carefully "—I can wait and book for the afternoon shuttle again tomorrow."

Deep in the basement the heater banged twice, gusting a long breath of hot air through the vents before switching back. Red-pink petals of the poinsettia plant on the table stirred and then were still.

Peripherally, Shelly noticed those things along with Richard Robert's monotonous ba-hum. She heard the thunderous tick of the wall clock and the rush of blood to her head. Her vision tunneled as it filled with the question in Dan's dark eyes.

"You'd want to stay longer?" She lifted a hand, sweeping it through the air in a vague gesture that seemed to encompass the occupants in the house, the building itself, each separate incident that had taken place in it and the hill the house was built upon. "With me? Here?"

Dan shrugged. "I doubt the boss would fire me for taking an extra day or two," he said, a husky note behind the smile in his voice. He continued to wait, holding his palm over the receiver.

Shelly knew exactly what he was asking. She also knew that now was the time to lock her heart back in its box and see him quickly to the door.

Her gaze left his to wander before settling on Richard Robert standing just outside the kitchen. She almost wished Dan's question had to do with her brother so that she would have something to hide behind. But that wasn't the case. Whether or not Dan left in four hours or twenty-four would take nothing away from Richard Robert. Regardless of her answer, he was on his way home.

The issue here was whether Shelly Barker was brave enough to admit out loud that she wanted Dan Sutherland to stay another night. The issue was whether she had enough courage to bypass the sensible reasons why he shouldn't stay. It would be, she knew, more sensible to hide behind excuses. She was terrified of making another mistake.

And yet, she knew if she didn't take the chance, Dan would go. The end. Confronted pointblank, the one thought was as terrifying as the other.

"I... we could..." she began, feeling her mouth shake. She wished Dan would hold out his hand. She wished he'd give her just one sign to let her know that her answer was half as important to him as it was hard for her. She tried a smile. "If you stayed, we could make up for... misunderstandings."

"Sure?" Dan held himself still. Her words conjured ghosts from the night before; sweet, hot specters of intense pleasure and banked emotion. The memory of unfinished business arced between them. Unanswered questions hovered in the silence.

He'd stormed in Friday night, assuming then that he'd had a right, giving little if any thought to what she wanted. Now, waiting for her answer, he trembled inside. Shelly had to want him to stay enough to commit herself. It had to be her decision.

Her breath was a mere thread of sound, but her answer was positive. "I'm sure."

Dan nodded. Never taking his gaze off her, he lifted the receiver to finish his call. The tiny smile trembling around her mouth slowly ventured upward and shyly lighted the blue glitter of her eyes. She was, he decided, wary as all hell and frightened enough to be shivering with it, but his gallant little warrior was brave. The relief was enough to humble him, rob him of triumph and arrogance.

It took a moment to finish the call and another one after that to admit to himself that he owed her an offer. The last step was to push the words past his reluctant lips. "I'm not simply assuming that you want me to sleep here." Dan cleared his throat. "I can stay with a cousin or in a hotel."

Shelly went to the counter, reached into the overhead cabinet for a mug and tried to fill it with nonexistent coffee from an empty carafe. When she realized what she was doing, she shook the glass container in bewilderment, as if she couldn't understand where the stuff had gone.

"You could do that," she said slowly, keeping her eyes down. No, she thought, if they were going to proceed with this relationship, they were going to do it honestly. She held out her hand, saw the tremor and put it behind her back. "But I would really like it if you stayed here."

"I wouldn't want to put you out."

It was a crazy thing to say after commandeering every hour of the last forty-eight, but it was what he could think of. Dan studied the tips of his fine leather shoes. Awkward, for a moment, he didn't know how to act. For all he knew, Shelly did her best work on Sundays.

There it was, Shelly thought and, muscle by muscle the trembling in her body eased. The sign. Dan Sutherland of the Denver branch of Sutherlands was perilously close to scuffling his feet while a faint red hue tinted the arch of his cheekbones. That wash of nervous color was the most beautiful she had ever seen.

A smile of mixed emotions played at the edge of her mouth. "No problem at all," she said, suddenly feeling giddy. "I normally pick up the Sunday paper after I drop Richard Robert off. How do you feel about enchiladas?"

Dan looked at Shelly. Slowly, the corner of his mouth pulled up. "Depends on who's doing the cooking. Me or you?"

"That depends," she echoed, and calculation shaded her voice, "on who gets the crossword puzzle."

Dan leaned a hip against the wall, folded his arms across his chest and sent her a smile full of charm and guile and phony innocence. "I do, don't I? I'm the guest."

Since she lived alone and worked from home, there was no such thing as a normal work routine in Shelly's life. She had a tendency to stay with a commission until it was finished, whether the assignment demanded eight hours or eighty. When working, days or even weeks meant little to her. With one exception.

*Sunday!* The word was as powerful as a mantra. *Sunday!* Conjuring up images of hedonistic idleness and self-indulgent excess. No housework, no errands, no obligations, no business or bookwork. No have-tos allowed. In the freezer, just waiting for attention, were packages of cream-filled, rum-layered, chocolate-iced pastries. Nestled in a place of honor was a cheesecake so decadent, it was wrapped in plain brown paper and smuggled in after dark.

Depending on her mood, Shelly had a new mystery novel for excitement and a historical for sizzle. If she wanted wine, it was in the pantry, and good friends were a phone call away. With keys to a car, she could go anywhere. With money in her pocket, she could do most anything. The time was hers to savor, relish, wallow in.

And this one, this Sunday, she had more than she'd ever dared dream. She had Dan Sutherland.

Nerves kept her jittery after dropping Richard Robert off at the group home. It was just as well that Dan had offered to drive back. When they stopped for the paper, excitement shook her fingers, made her clumsy as change spilled over the counter. Panic shriveled any conversation she might have made on the drive back up the hill. Her wits scattered, and she couldn't collect them. The ride home was silent and endless.

There were times during the afternoon when she felt she couldn't breathe. The feeling, a combination of exhilaration and fear, caught in her chest, made her stomach clench and quiver.

It was a kind of claustrophobia. She would sit next to Dan on the couch and watch him read the newspaper. Then her eyes would drift to his hands and she would remember how they had felt on her. She couldn't be still. Those times she would stumble in her haste to get up... away... out.

"Shelly!" Dan's section of the newspaper rattled as he tossed it aside. His reflexes proved quick enough so that when he stuck out his stockinged toe, he snagged it under the hem of her baggy sweatshirt, caught her off balance and hauled her back down. It was the sixth bolt in less than thirty minutes, and he was ready to howl.

"I promise, darlin'...I swear to you...I'm not going to pounce. You are absolutely safe on this couch with me."

Some of the tension went out of her. "I'm sorry," she whispered, and her shoulders slumped. "I'm an idiot."

"You're not." Dan reached out a finger to hook a fire-bright curl around the small shell of her ear.

"Yes, I am," Shelly insisted, shivering at his touch. She could continue to huddle in misery or go back to her own side. Or she could wrestle him to the floor, have her way and get the thing over. She scooted to the far corner of the couch and picked up the business-opportunities section one more time.

"It'll be easier to read if you turn the page right-side up." Dan smiled crookedly. During the past hour, he'd wanted nothing more than to shake her. He'd wanted to laugh, or alternatively, to gnash his teeth. Now he wanted to hold her. "If you don't calm down, you're going to make us both cry."

She kept her eyes blindly fixed on the paper, and said in a small, quick voice, "Sorry."

Pushing his section of the paper aside, Dan shifted his position so that he was more reclining than sitting, his back in the corner against the high, cushioned armrest and his legs stretched out atop the cushions toward her. He made a place for her and held out his hand.

"Come here, Shelly. After staying up all night last night, you're too tired to make sense. What you need is a nap."

"A nap?" Shelly blinked, wondering if he was joking. He was sprawled along the length of the couch, calmly patting the space he expected her to occupy. Her gaze slowly moved from the heavy muscles of his spread thighs upward to meet and lock with his enigmatic brown eyes.

"You honestly expect me to lie between your legs...drape myself against your chest...*and take a nap?*" Springing to her feet, she began to stalk the room. "I'd have to be a hundred years old." Her gestures got wilder as she paced from the window to the door then back to the couch. "I look at you and shake, and you want me to *sleep?* Maybe I could if I were dead."

She shook her head and whirled back around. "I realize this is easy for you, just another weekend, but I can't pretend. I haven't made love with anyone in two years...I'm scared...and I really, really want to... with you."

Using his toe, Dan snagged her again under the hem of her sweatshirt; easy enough to do when the baggy material puffed and billowed around her narrow hips. And since he caught her in midstride, it only needed a flex of his leg to reel her closer. A jerk of his foot brought her down next to him.

"Do you get 'easy' from this, Shelly?" He took her hand and pressed it against his chest where his heart pumped hard and erratic under her palm. Holding her gaze, he slowly moved her hand down his body until it trembled, as it had the night before around the straining fullness of his erection. He closed her fingers around him. When her eyes widened and her breath hissed, he moved her hand back up to his chest.

"Contrary to what you think, this is not 'easy' for me." His voice was a deep, controlled rumble, shaded with the merest thread of humor. "I am not feeling particularly placid...but darlin', Richard Robert only left us one untrashed party balloon, remember? I don't want to waste it in a quick flash. I want a slow burn, later, with you."

A shudder of anticipation and then an overwhelming exhaustion left her suddenly reeling. Shelly slumped. "Have you guessed yet that I'm not much good at this mature-relationship stuff?"

Dan ignored her question. "I think we should forget the relationship...too hard on the nerves. Let's just get married."

"What about Richard Robert? He was in a good mood this weekend. Wait until he gets cranky. He's not going to go away."

"Neither am I."

"Yeah?" She lifted a hand to his cheek. "That's what they all say. I don't need promises, Dan."

"We *both* need a nap. How about if we agree to hold off any deep discussions or ravishment of each other until later, okay?"

With little energy left, Shelly felt herself being shifted and resettled. Dan's hands stroked and eased her up onto his lap. When his arms came around her, she gave up all pretence and concentrated on taking deep, slow breaths. Minutes passed and her eyelids got heavier. His hard body relaxed and the swift drum of his heart steadied to a calm, reassuring beat.

She didn't want to recognize the symptoms of what ailed her, but she was very much afraid she might be developing an incurable case.

Shelly wasn't dreaming. No dream had such rich, dark tastes. Fantasies didn't have these vivid textures and exotic scents. She was aware of each separate finger on the hand that drew through her hair, stroking from her nape to the base of her spine. She knew the moment Dan's head lowered and she sensed the first ghost kiss he brushed across her cheekbone. She felt the smile on his lips as she tilted her face to accommodate more of those phantom caresses.

The same smile was in his voice as he accused, "I know you're awake." Leisurely, he struck at her most vulnerable pulse points, a gentle nip at her earlobe, a lick along the curve of her bottom lip, a sip when she opened her mouth to let him in. "Wanna fool around?"

She opened her eyes and deliberately let go of all shoulds and oughts and have-tos. She turned loose her fear. Looking straight into Dan's gleaming brown eyes, she returned his smile with a long, languid one of her own. "Yeah."

Dan went very still. One perfect, sable eyebrow began an incremental ascent toward his hairline. "Now?"

Drawing back, Shelly considered. Excitement began to bubble in her blood and through her body, growing into a drunk, giddy feeling. His shirt was a wrinkled mess, the top two buttons undone, and she leaned over to drop a kiss in the hollow of his throat.

"No, not now," she said, and laughed. If they only had one condom, she wanted to do it right. Her cheeks flushed and the color soon rivaled the deep reds glinting in her hair. "I don't want to make love with you when I'm all musty, rumpled and groggy."

For their night together, she wanted to smell of expensive perfume and tempt like sin. There was a stage to set. Shelly wanted romance.

Dan understood her need. He gave her a helping shove off the couch, grinning as she tumbled to the floor. Damned if he didn't want all the trimmings, too. "We'll make dinner and light candles."

Shelly nodded eagerly. "We'll savor."

"God, yes. We'll—" He fell back with a short bark of laughter. "Is that all we've got? One? I don't suppose you have any other kind of protection stashed away for a rainy day?"

Shelly looked away. "No, I...no." She went on to admit, "I thought about it when we stopped to buy the newspaper, but I didn't want to appear too...anxious."

"And I—" Dan threw his arm across his eyes and heaved a sigh of amused disgust "—didn't want you to think sex was the only reason I wanted to stay."

Shelly rose on her knees and pushed his arm away so that she could peer into his face. "You didn't want to make love with me tonight?"

He pulled her closer, nose to nose, and growled, "You bet I did! What I said was, I didn't want you to think it was the *only* reason."

"So what do we do?"

"Why, darlin'—" he folded his hands behind his head, and his smile returned along with a wicked glint that lit his dark eyes with a hundred pinpoints of amber "—just what we've been doing. We choose our moment."

Shelly owned a bottle of champagne. An excellent vintage, the clerk had assured her when she'd bought it. The kind used at the grandest of openings, for the wedding toast, the baby's christening or—the clerk's eyebrows had wagged—that special anniversary. Tonight would be all those things and more.

Tonight was for celebrating.

Already she'd plumped pillows and lit the candles so that the room would be scented and waiting. There were no violins, but she had classic Rod Stewart.

Shelly also owned a teddy. Even though she could make anything she wanted for herself, she'd seen this one in an exclusive lingerie shop at the mall and bought it. The teal green, raw silk confection had been in her drawer for nearly three years. The tags still hung from an inside seam, attached by a tiny gold-colored safety pin. She'd never worn the thing; not simply for her own enjoyment; never for anyone else. Shelly had never felt . . . enough . . . to wear it.

Tonight was for bravery.

Standing in front of the mirror in her bedroom, all perfumed and lotioned from a shower, she held the teddy up to her chest. Maybe later, with candlelight filling in hollows, and champagne to blur edges . . . and Dan. She would put it on under her clothes, and they could take hours of time unwrapping each other. When they touched, she could pretend that she really wouldn't change back into a toad when the clock struck midnight.

"May I come in?"

Shelly turned, sweeping the teddy behind her back. He *was* in, and she didn't believe that little-boy-lost look for a minute.

"I'm lonely out there by myself...slaving away over a pan of frozen enchiladas. I don't know why *I* have to preheat the oven." Dan came farther into the room, a look of amused curiosity tilting his mouth. "What are you doing?"

There was no way Shelly could ditch the bit of silk. Crushing the fabric into a ball, she felt ridiculous for even pulling it out. Frowning, with her free hand, she groped for the drawer handle.

"What are you doing?" Dan repeated patiently.

No use. "I wanted to get ready for you," Shelly admitted in a small, rueful voice. Lamely, she held up the teddy, tags dangling. "I wanted to be glamorous and irresistible and... I'm not exactly the type."

"Shelly Barker, you worry about foolish, foolish things." He came up behind, put his hands on her shoulders. They stood together facing the long dresser mirror. She came up to his heart, and her hair was brilliant against the pale blue of his shirt. Where he was shadow, she was light. His hands were large and dark against the pale delicacy of her skin. He reached to push her hair aside and bent to kiss the tender nape. "Do you know what I see?"

Her heart had begun to scramble like a wild thing. Only the stark intensity of his expression in the mirror held her upright. Words were beyond her, but the question was there as she watched him pick up her hand.

"I see," he said, holding her reflected gaze captive with his own and kissing her fingertips, "independence."

He brought her hand up just a bit higher and opened the fingers with his thumb. He brushed his lips across her tender palm. "Competence."

When his mouth moved to her wrist, he murmured, "Strength." At the crook of her elbow he found, "loyalty." When he was done, her arm dropped limply to her side.

Then he angled his head and sought her mouth. "Humor." He dallied at the corner. "Passion." His breath fell soft and warm against her eyelids. "Intelligence," he whispered, kissing them closed.

When he had her limp, leaning back against him, he brushed his hands over the bright fall of her hair down to her shoulders and turned her around. "I see you, Shelly. You're beautiful."

The straight path Shelly had been walking for the past two years dropped right out from beneath her feet. She just hadn't expected it to happen so soon or so completely. When morning came, and it would, she had no idea what she would do. But for now, she wanted nothing more than to make love with this incredible man.

Taking his hand, she led him to the bed. Her bed. "Now, please." When his fingers went to the buttons of his shirt, she pushed them away and smiled into his eyes. "Let me."

She felt glorious and strong, an Amazon standing before him with nothing more on than a shaky smile. No need to hide behind silk or lace. He was the beautiful one. He gave her freedom. They tumbled onto the bed, and she rose up on her knees above him. Whatever she wanted she could have. He threw back his head when she reached for him. No half measures. No holding back. She absorbed him, made him weak, and he let her see.

He was the strongest man she had ever known. And the most gentle. He put his mouth and hands to her breasts and made her feel...enough. More than enough. She'd never dreamed that a man would look at her as Dan did. As if she was all he wanted, as if she was precious. He lingered over her mouth, her shoulder blades and belly, the bright nest of curls between her legs.

And when she was trembling, slick and wet and shivering, he paused for a moment to sheath himself, then entered her.

It was just as Dan thought it would be. More. Shelly burned around him, all bright, flashing energy. Nothing coy here, nothing planned or practiced. The silky heat of her was so tight that her sharp little cry was all it took. Despite his years and experience, his control was nonexistent. When he felt the first faint convulsions of her climax, he grit his teeth, waited just long enough to assure her release, and then went with her. Over the edge.

"What do you want Santa to bring you for Christmas, little red-headed girl?"

It took too much effort to smile. If Shelly could have, she would have pinched him. Somehow they'd ended up with Dan sprawled diagonally across the rumpled bed and Shelly, equally sated, draped across him.

"Nothing, now." She turned her face into his shoulder to stifle a yawn. "I just got my present. What do you want, pretty brown-eyed boy?"

"That's easy." He laughed. "I want the little red-headed girl." He forced his hand to move, tangling his fingers in her hair. "What are we having for Christmas dinner?"

Shelly's inert body tensed. "Christmas dinner?"

"Umm, you know, the big festive banquet you're supposed to prepare the morning after Christmas Eve. I like cranberry sauce... the jelly kind, not the lumpy stuff."

"No lumps," she promised, and added casually, "Richard Robert will be here."

"Oh." Dan went quiet, then said, "I'll have to put in an appearance at my mother's bash."

"I'll have him the whole Christmas week."

"Listen—" he moved, shifting just enough so that she slipped from his chest into the crook of his arm "—am I invited for dinner or not?"

Shelly closed her eyes. What had she been thinking? That Dan would simply stay until morning and then disappear? Had she honestly believed it would be so cut-and-dried? No, his relationships would be infinitely civilized and caring. He was a good man, a sensitive one. He wasn't the kind to slink away in the night. When he left, he'd do his best to go gently. And Shelly knew that even a heart in a million pieces eventually mended.

His arm was hooked around her neck as if he meant to keep her there, and his face was close. If she had had the energy, she would have glared. The best she could do was a mild accusation. "You're a damned pushy man."

"Yeah, so?"

She drew back and studied him. "So? So don't expect mincemeat pie for dessert, that's what. My aversion to egg slime is nothing compared to raisin mud."

"Deal," Dan growled, then he laughed and rolled over with her. "And now we've got that settled... do you want to help me count how many ways there are to make love without *really* making love?"

## *Chapter Twelve*

Music was a subtle accompaniment to the ebb and flow of laughter and sophisticated party chatter. Not for the first time, Dan wondered where his mother managed to find her cast of characters. Securing a vapory blonde, draped from neck to toe in black, who could strum old-style English carols on a lute couldn't have been an easy task. Linda had to have stretched her formidable creative talents to come up with that one, he decided.

The annual Denver Christmas Eve bash was a success. For Linda Sutherland, nothing else was acceptable.

A fleet of silent-footed waiters circulated through the milling crowds, distributing spiced wassail punch and imported ale with balletic finesse. The small army of red-liveried men all appeared to be in their early twenties, similar in physical stature and darkly picturesque. Had they arrived with the caterer, from a casting director or had his mother simply had them cloned for tonight's event?

Lifting a crystal glass containing his father's best Grand Marnier to his mouth, Dan let the liquid touch his lips. He wasn't in the mood for drinking, much less in a mood to charm any of the one hundred or so people teeming through his parents' home. Of course, he knew he was expected to circulate. As his father's son, he had obligations to family friends and business associates.

Dan hadn't forgotten his duties; he simply needed a few moments outside of them.

For the second time in less than a month, he found himself backed into a corner at a party. Around him, holiday revelers partook in an unending supply of food and drink. Depending upon the speaker, the talk was idle, malicious, boring or amusing.

There were other noticeable differences between this Christmas celebration and that one. Tonight there were no wheelchairs, no protective helmets worn with the elegant dinner jackets and not one bright head of orangey red hair darting through the crowd.

During the course of the evening, Dan came to the conclusion that a full two-thirds of the women in the house must have been blond, from the matronly silver-haired variety to the long-legged, honey-blonde across the room.

"Thinking of buying stock in her company...or just planning on adding a little extra something to your Christmas list?" Ty Sutherland asked as he, too, sipped from a bowl shaped glass. The men had gravitated to the same corner for respite.

Ty's speculative gaze had followed his cousin's absent one across the room and come to rest on the same attractive honey-blonde. "Judging by the way she's been watching this corner, either one of us would qualify as her Christmas bonus."

Exaggerated amusement registered on Dan's face once he realized the lady's interest and his cousin's misinterpretation of his own. "Ty," he said, lifting his glass in a mock salute, "as your elder and better, I feel I ought to point out a slight flaw in your character."

"I'll give you older." Ty turned his head, and the habitually hard edge to the curve of his mouth was gone. In its place was a rare humor that only a few close and most-trusted people ever witnessed. "But I deny the better. Okay, I'll bite. What's wrong with my character?"

Undaunted, Dan returned the smile. "You are a cynical bastard."

Ty took his time mulling over the pronouncement. A sound, suspiciously like laughter, was quickly cleared away. His eyes narrowed slyly. "You want to repeat the illegitimate part of that charge in front of my mother?"

Dan's lips twitched as he looked back out over the gathered assembly. "Not a chance."

"Speaking of my mother..."

"Were we?" Dan did nothing to hide his amusement. Since Ty's arrival earlier this evening, he'd had a hunch they'd be getting around to this conversation. "How is Megan?"

Ty grunted. "As nosy as ever. Since I lost the draw this year, anyway—"

"Don't let *my* mother hear you say that."

"Hell, everyone knows we draw straws to determine which one of us gets stuck flying across the Rockies on Christmas Eve."

"Not everyone."

"Don't kid yourself. That delicate little tank you call Mama simply chooses not to know what a chore this is for the rest of us." When there was no sound of disagreement, Ty switched back to his original tack. "Speaking of tanks, you don't owe anyone an account of what goes on in your private life, but could you give me one statement to take back home. Hell, anything will do. Just enough to satisfy my dear old mum's curiosity."

"Tell Meggie—" Dan couldn't decide which would be the safest admission, that he was deadly serious about Shelly Barker or that Shelly believed being serious was deadly. "Tell her... the verdict isn't in yet."

"Is that supposed to make sense?"

Dan gave his cousin a hard, direct look. "Not one bit of sense."

"Dan?" With ease and familiarity, a dark-haired young woman in an extravagantly expensive green dress slipped under his arm. "You're making those obscene finger gestures again."

A second young woman, nearly an exact replica of the first, instigated herself against the weight of Ty's strong shoulder. "Those aren't obscene gestures," she said, quickly defending her brother, pushing a heavy pair of glasses back upon her thin nose, "that's the manual alphabet used by the deaf of North America. Dan's learning to sign."

"How do you know that's what he's doing?" Katherine Sutherland challenged her twin sister, Quynn. "He's been doing bizarre things for days. I say he's been practicing some explicitly obscene finger gestures." She tilted her head up to look up at him. "And once he figures them out, he's going to teach me."

"You've got it, baby." Growling with laughter, Dan bent his head to drop a kiss on his sister's cheek. "What brings you both over to our dark corner?"

Quynn answered, giving her glasses another shove. "We just thought you should know that Mr. and Mrs. Penderton have arrived, and they've brought their niece from California...Melinda." She drew the name out as if it left an oddly sour taste on her tongue. "Melinda is recently divorced and absolutely thrilled to be here. Mum is on the watch out for you two and has *the* glazed look on her face."

The men exchanged a quick glance of understanding. They both knew exactly what *the* look on Linda Sutherland's face meant.

A half-formed expletive came from Ty.

"Wait," Katherine said, cutting him off, and holding up her hand. "Can you finger-spell that?" Dan had mastered enough of the alphabet so that he could, and did, repeat the curse in sign.

"Okay, here's the plan," he said quickly. "We'll grace this party with forty-five minutes more of 'cousinly' charm. Rendezvous time is eleven-fifteen, upstairs in the old playroom. Katherine, you let Dad know. Quynn, you're in charge of the feast...anything but that damn pâté she's got spread down the buffet table. Ty, you get the Christmas presents Aunt Megan sent over. I'll work on the bubbly."

Ty consulted his watch. "Forty-five minutes should give all of you enough time to round up *my* presents and get them upstairs." His mock frown grew more pointed as he singled out each of the young women. "You *did* remember to make this trip worth my time."

"Boxes of goodies," Quynn vowed blithely, unaffected by his formidable scowl.

Katherine gave her sister backing. "You'll have to rent a cargo plane to get it all home this year. Why... uh-oh, look out."

"Damn," Ty muttered balefully.

"Upstairs, forty-five minutes, bring the loot," Dan ordered. "Now... scatter."

By the time Linda Sutherland, less than half a room away, managed to work through the crowd to the corner where she'd last seen her family, they'd all vanished. She turned to Melinda Penderton with a puzzled frown. "I'm sorry, my dear, I could have sworn they were right here."

Ties loosened, formal jackets long-since shed, five people sat comfortably around a warm hearth. The noise from downstairs was blocked out by solid, well-constructed walls and a firmly closed door. Quynn, perched on the arm of her father's chair, opened one of the last of the gifts. All eyes were upon her as she meticulously peeled each piece of tape from the brightly wrapped package.

"Hurry up," Katherine urged impatiently from the shelter of her brother's side on the long, low sofa. "You drive me crazy."

Dan had pulled young Katherine down next to him and while her soft weight against his shoulder was familiar, it did nothing to quiet his restless, inner dance of turbulence. He wanted to be gone.

A hand's drop away were packages of every size and description, all things a man could want and more: cashmere sweaters; silk shirts and ties; elegant trinkets; absurd trifles. Dan was, indeed, a fortunate man, but more than once lately, he'd found himself massaging his chest in the vicinity of his heart, searching over his shoulder.

The girl's soft laughter played around him, his father's and cousin's deeper voices added and blended with the sound to create a symphony of relaxed contentment. The war of impatience inside him raged on.

"I love my present." Katherine's voice brought Dan's thoughts back to the gathering. Her soft kiss on his chin made him smile. She held a fist-sized, flawless sphere of transparent Australian crystal in her hands, turning it occasionally to examine the many facets. "Now whenever anyone asks how I know things, I'll just say I saw it in my magic ball."

"That was the whole idea," Dan told her quietly. "Keep it out where skeptics can see, look them right in the eye and don't apologize."

"Got it," his sister quipped, grinning. "Either that or learn to keep my mouth shut." The smile left her face. "Dan . . . she'd fit in here. She would like us."

Dan didn't bother to ask Katherine how she knew the direction of his thoughts, nor did he need to clarify what or whom she was referring to. Long ago he'd stopped questioning his sister's gift of sensitivity. So acute were her powers of observation that there were times when she seemed to know what he was thinking before he did. Sometimes, like now, her insights were uncanny.

Dipping his head closer, his voice matched the curiosity in his smiling eyes. "Did you *see* for me, Katy?"

"It's not hard to guess you've had a lot on your mind," she said, sidestepping his question. "You haven't been yourself since you got home."

"How do you know it's a woman?"

Katherine laughed softly. "The first clue was the strange things you've been doing with your fingers. You've been moody, distracted . . . as if the body remains but your brain leaves and . . . you've called me Shelly—twice." She hesitated. "Can I add something else?"

"What is it?"

"Please be very happy. You lead the way for us all."

"What about Debra? She's already made the commitment I'm only considering."

Katherine hesitated, obviously searching for words. "It will happen for Debra...but—" she shrugged "—maybe not this time. Besides, Ty and Kiall don't notice Debra. They'll be looking to *you* to show them how."

"What are you two plotting?" Ty asked, breaking into the murmured conversation, bringing everyone's attention around to the whispering pair.

"Dan and his lady," Katherine answered simply. She switched her clear gaze to her father. "He's defecting to the West, Daddy. You should be the one to talk to mother about this... *after* he's gone."

"Hold on." Amused more than irritated, Dan put his hand over his sister's mouth. "Katy, as usual, is jumping in before checking the water level. I am considering such a move, but the lady still needs a lot of convincing."

"Treason," Ty charged, then burst out laughing, a hard, cynical sound. "Have you waved the family checkbook before her eyes? Try it... she'll come around."

Dan could only shake his head. "You're a suspicious man, Cousin, but you couldn't be more wrong. In fact, I'm sure Shelly would like it better if I was in a lower tax bracket. She's firmly convinced that I will not or cannot cope with what she considers to be real life."

"How dare she!" Quynn burst in loyally. "What in the world can she be thinking?"

"She's thinking of her brother...her retarded, deaf brother. I won't go into what happened when I met Richard Robert, but she has a point. In many ways, life will be different than what I'm used to."

"I believe if you can cope with your mother, the despot," Drew Sutherland said affectionately, though they all knew the truth of it, "—one sister who 'sees' things, another who knows everything—" he cleared his throat "—and with a cousin who reportedly eats human flesh for breakfast...sorry Ty, but that is the story I've heard lately."

Ty nodded his acknowledgment and added helpfully, "Don't forget my mother."

"Right...and with Megan's tendency to poke her curious nose into any place it's not appreciated, you stand a good chance of managing your lady's relatives."

A slow, self-mocking smile stretched across Dan's mouth. "I thought the very same thing. The only remaining glitch is convincing Shelly."

The house was quiet, the party long since over, when Ty found his cousin alone in the downstairs library.

"Catch."

A small metal object flew threw the air and into the hand Dan instinctively extended to retrieve it. Opening his fingers, he stared at the key, then lifted a questioning glance to the man across the room.

"Think of it as a Christmas present," Ty muttered, stalking to a window that overlooked the driveway. "I'm not going to give you a hard time about this thing you've got going with the dressmaker...even though I think it's one of the most ridiculously asinine things you've ever considered."

Dan's eyebrows lifted, and he smiled at his cousin's forbearance. "Thanks."

"The key is to my place in the valley." Ty ran his fingers through his hair, his face quietly serious. "I figure if you're set on defecting, you'll need a base camp."

Dan's hand closed around the key. This time when he looked at his cousin, there was no mockery in his smile. "Thank you."

"Don't waste your gratitude," Ty said gruffly. "I'm not doing you a favor. The idea behind the key is to give you a place to clear your head. When it looks as though she's winning...use it."

"Ty, not all women are soulless witches." Dan's expression was somber, his voice calm, utterly certain. "The war doesn't have to be bloody."

Ty turned away, his voice laced with amused contempt. "Think what you like, Cousin, you usually do." He shrugged the subject away. "Well, I've done the family duty, and now I'm headed west, San Diego, I think, or Vegas.

Don't expect to see me in Salt Lake any time soon. I don't want to be there. The thought of watching an intelligent man...grovel leaves a nasty aftertaste."

"Grovel?" Dan mouthed the word, rolling the flavor of it around on his tongue. No, he decided, not the right description at all, and he corrected his cousin as Ty walked to the door. "It's more like being shoved headfirst over a cliff onto a hard, flat rock...repeatedly. After a while, the senseless feeling begins to make sense."

Ty stared back at him curiously. A moment went by, then he lifted his hand in a mocking farewell. "So long, Dan. If anyone asks why I didn't stay for Christmas breakfast, tell them I lost my appetite."

Dan wouldn't be around to deliver the message. He didn't plan on staying for breakfast, either; had a seat booked on the 7:30 a.m. flight out of Stapleton. He shrugged and let his cousin get almost through the door, nearly away, before delivering his parting remark.

"Don't get too comfortable in your rut, Ty. Katherine saw it all, and according to her, you'll definitely be getting yours."

Outside, a thin Christmas snow fell from a black, heavy sky. The quiet was disturbed by the faint thud of a slamming door somewhere upstairs and the monotonous tick of a generations-old grandfather clock out in the wide, tiled foyer.

Dan rested his head against the supple leather of his father's favorite chair and studied the angles of a plain, brown telephone across the wide, polished desk.

During the past few weeks, the impulse to pick up that phone and call Shelly had intensified until it had become a tight coil of urgency in the pit of Dan's belly.

Sometimes when he looked down to find his hand reaching out, when he swore to himself that the sound of her voice would be enough, it took a powerful effort of will to pull his hand back and think...patience.

The question of whether he would go back had never been an issue, at least not in his mind. But this time it would be different. Without a clue, he'd stepped into Shelly Barker's world and stumbled. Only a fool would try it again without careful preparation.

Leaving the chair, Dan walked to the window. The question of logistics and time were finally settled. Simple enough, really. Dan had decided to pack up his Rolodex and the rest of his office, lock, stock and fax machine, and resume his familial obligations on the west side of the Rockies.

He ran his finger over the serrated edge of the key his cousin had given him. A well-meant but useless gesture. Dan had no intention of using the thing. She didn't know it yet, but he planned on settling in with Shelly Barker, for the duration.

There were different kinds of cold: the icy sweat of fear; the chill of one body in a bed meant for two. Empty arms, solitary dinners, cold heart. Shelly stood for a long time by the window.

She should have gone to bed hours ago, but first there had been Richard Robert—her trusting, man-child brother; old enough to know that Santa Claus never really came, yet hoping, wanting it so badly that he had been impossible to settle.

There were piles of presents under the tree, but Richard Robert had wanted none of it. Instead, he'd paced by the fireplace for hours, waiting for one, just one, sign or glimpse that what he wished to believe was true.

Now Shelly stood alone in her workroom and looked out at nothing at all.

Waiting for Dan made her crazy. She wasn't the kind of woman who thought only a man could make her whole. She didn't want or need to be rescued. Yet here she was in the dark, expecting...wanting more while hope and dread battled for dominance in the pit of her stomach. She cursed herself because she knew better. No one had to tell her that she was acting as unrealistically as her brother.

She could not sleep. Thoughts chased and circled in her brain. Dan was coming.

She worried. More than a half dozen packages had been delivered throughout the past week, and she'd stacked them all under the tree. Two of the presents were designated for Richard Robert. The rest bore her name.

Though she had looked and looked, agonized and debated, she'd only been able to find one gift to give in return. What if Dan expected more? What if...?

Forcing her thoughts onto something else, Shelly moved away from the window and returned to the worktable. The sketch of the gown was almost perfect, she decided. The pencil rendering nearly matched the vision in her mind right down to the last opalescent seed pearl on the high choker collar.

Funny thing about this one. She rarely had the time or energy these days to work on anything not already commissioned. And when she did, an original free-hand design normally took hours of sketching and revising to get right. This one had come as if from a dream to the paper. If Dan had called her, just once, she might have chatted with him about the gown. She'd have told him how effortlessly it had come and how strange that was. But he had not called. Her only word from him had been a short note in the last package.

The gown began with intricate Venetian lace over a straight, calf-length, ivory silk sheath. The sleeves were full batwing, tapering to a two-inch cuff with the same delicate banding of pearls as on the collar and lacy, handkerchief hem. Inexplicably, Shelly had continued to sketch right down to fine details. The faceless model came complete with pale stockings, ankle high, ivory satin button boots and a wide-brimmed garden hat. It was a vision of simplicity and nostalgia, of romance and innocence.

The gown would be expensive to complete and time-consuming to execute; it was a gamble without a confirmed buyer. Shelly had had to wait over nine months for her supplier to get that one bolt of ivory silk. The value, to her, was nearly priceless. And yet for this gown, nothing less would do.

Dan would be arriving in the morning; his note had said so. The sun would be up by nine, all dark and shadow gone. A glance at her watch read three hours after midnight, not so many left.

For days she'd dithered between fixing a traditional turkey or ham dinner. In the end she had prepared both and frozen all. A housecleaning frenzy struck midweek and lasted three days. Not one cobweb was left floating. Locked away in her bathroom vanity was a new prescription of birth-control pills.

Richard Robert knew they were expecting company, she had given him fair warning. If he hadn't actually promised to be good, at least he had agreed to be... reasonable.

The flush of anticipation was as painful as anything Shelly had ever felt. While Richard Robert had worn himself out wanting and waiting for Santa, Shelly stood alone in her workroom on Christmas Eve... waiting for another Prince Charming.

## *Chapter Thirteen*

Shelly wasn't sure what she had expected.

A freeze frame, maybe, like in an old movie. Dan would pull into the driveway; she would come to the door. All movement would cease. A lot of intense eye contact, maybe some lip trembling. Then the camera would pull back and she would somehow waft down the steps toward him . . . above the snow, of course, so her chiffon didn't get wet...to meet him at the white picket fence, where she would fall into his arms and they would cover each other with kisses.

There was a bit of eye contact, but it wasn't affection Shelly first saw in the biting blast of Dan's brown eyes. And she didn't waft down the steps when he finally pulled into her driveway, over an eternity late.

She stumbled in her own agitation to find out where the sweet hell he'd been. It was lucky for them both that the white picket fence was only in her imagination, otherwise she might have tripped over it when Dan's glowering countenance emerged from the interior of the car. Or alternatively, she'd have wrenched out one of the wooden slats and taken a home-run swing at his perfect head.

"It's close to eleven. Your note said nine. Two hours!"

"Damn right, two hours! How long did you think I'd wait?"

"*You've* been waiting? I've imagined you dead or dying in every mountain crevasse from here to Denver. They wouldn't tell me, you know, your family. Why would they? I'd have to read about you in the paper. Where have you been?"

"All I want to know is why? Was it too much trouble? No, wait, let me guess. In the end...in what you believe will be the end...you won't be held responsible for the outcome if I initiated the relationship and I made all the moves. Of course, I can see now why you couldn't pick me up from the airport. Too much of a commitment on your part, right? A personal declaration, maybe too personal for you, hmm, Shelly?"

Dan, angry, was a formidable man.

Formidable enough to awe Shelly into silence—for one moment only. How was she supposed to know that he had expected her to pick him up at the airport? His note hadn't said, 'Shelly, come get me.' She had forgotten rule number three in the good old code-of-ethics book. The third tenet stated something to the effect that one of a lower caste...or a female...was to always know what Prince Charming wanted, whether or not he made his wishes clear or even knew them himself.

"*I,*" she said sweetly as she smiled and began moving with concentrated attention across the snowy sidewalk, "would have been at the airport." She kept her voice bland so that she didn't alert him before she could start chewing like an enraged dwarf Doberman. "If *you* had given one clue that that's what you expected. Any little thing would have done... another two-sentence note... a bang on your war drum... a collect call."

What should have been obvious was her relief that he hadn't crashed and been frozen solid in some high-mountain pass. And her disappointment. Cold wasn't the only reason her eyes were watering. Her own expectations of this reunion scene lay in fragments around her feet.

Had Dan directed his attention to the house, he would have seen the damned silly lighted candle she'd put in the front window... at nine o'clock. By ten, the thing had guttered out. Being Christmas and all, she thought it would be appropriate... and for Shelly, the oversentimentality of the gesture *was* a declaration.

She stared straight at him, as angry as she'd ever been and getting madder. "Not a single phone call. You could have given me that, Dan... one lousy call."

Days of frustration had worn away any claim Dan had ever had to patience, while nights of sleeplessness had left his temper ragged edged. He closed his eyes and clenched his teeth so hard, his jaw bulged. Why was it that of all the women he knew in the world, this one, this one skinny, orange-haired woman had the power to reduce him to the point of near incoherence?

She maddened him. A phone call? *Hell!* She was too damned obstinate to open her eyes and see that he was ready to give her the world, or at least share his corner of it with her.

She infuriated him. Not once, not ever, had he been left to cool his heels at an airport, anywhere for that matter. Humbling was the way to describe the experience and not one he wanted to repeat.

She... missed him. As the meaning behind her angry words sank in, Dan felt his own heat begin to cool. Okay, so she hadn't picked up on the hint he'd left in the note... *underlined* flight number, *exact* arrival time, *directions* to airline gate. He'd forgotten that Shelly Barker wasn't like the ordinary women he used to know. Next time, when he wanted to be subtle, he'd simply include a sledgehammer.

Shelly didn't say any more. She couldn't think of anything. She just stood there, staring at Dan while he stared right back and the tension of their weeks apart arced and spat between them.

There were a dozen questions she wanted answered. Was he well? He looked tired. Had he missed her? She'd marked every day off her calendar with slashing red pencil *x*'s. Had his days been as sterile and empty as hers had been? His night dreams as vivid and frustrating? How many times had he heard a voice or seen a flash of someone familiar and found himself looking over his shoulder?

"Shelly?" The flat, reasonable tone of Dan's voice brought her to sharp attention. "One of us is going to have to give, or we'll be out here all day. I'm not above taking the first step, but I need you to start taking a few in my direction, as well. Meet me halfway on this one."

There was silence for a moment. Shelly's head drooped on her slender neck as all the fight drained out of her. All right, so they'd had different expectations. He'd been waiting for a ride while she had burned a silly candle. Fair was fair and she knew it. So far in their relationship, Dan had been the generous one, giving one hundred percent.

As for her part, uncertainty kept her too rigid to yield. Fear had made her stingy.

A sudden, sharp bite of the December wind blew through her heavy sweater and she shivered, huddling deeper into the wool. Somewhere over and down in the next block a dog barked. Strands of her hair whipped across her face and she pushed them away. She felt small and mean, yet the conflict raged within her.

"I'm only asking for a few concessions, Shelly, not unconditional surrender."

Always that fine thread of humor. Slowly she raised her head and saw the small, whimsical curve at the corner of his mouth. He made it seem so easy. Despite the watery sting in her eyes and a runny nose, she almost smiled back. "Not yet, anyway."

"Just a few steps, darlin'. I'll do the rest."

She brushed a hand at her cheek and sniffed. "Hi," she whispered. "I've been waiting for you, Dan . . . a long time. If you'd like, I've got some coffee on, and hot cocoa and soup." She looked away, then back. "I've made you a turkey dinner...and a ham dinner...and a sweater, and...I'm so glad you're here." Clearing her throat, her last question was painful. "Is this still what you want to do?"

Dan tipped his head to one side and looked at her. And waited. "It is."

Shelly let out a long, shaky breath and took one faltering step toward him, then another. "Well, then, would you like to come inside? Get out of the cold?"

"Yeah," he said, "I'd like that. But first..." He closed the remaining distance and, cradling her upturned face between his hands, he bent to brush a kiss across her mouth. "Hello, Shelly Barker. I've missed you, too."

His lips were cold, but his breath fell in warm puffs against her skin. When she looked into his face, she saw amusement tugging at his mouth, and she felt a relief so vast, her knees nearly buckled. Everything, she decided, would be all right now.

She suddenly felt like grinning. "I was on the verge of a nervous breakdown, but now that you're here, it can wait. Wanna help me unwrap the goodies Santa brought?"

"What did Richard Robert think of his loot?"

"I'm sure he'll love it." She took his hand as they walked to the house, lacing her fingers through his, "as soon as he gets to open it. We've been waiting for you."

There was a certain terror in sublime happiness. For instance, Shelly didn't dare say the words aloud. To say something like, 'This is all I need,' could jinx the feeling, might cancel the mood. Happiness could be snatched away so easily. One had to be cautious—a pinch of salt over the shoulder, a pair of crossed fingers, a knock on wood.

But nothing could stop her from silently acknowledging the feeling, and if she was careful, not too blatant, she intended to revel in every moment that it lasted.

They hadn't got around to eating yet or opening the pile of presents stacked under the tree...except for one. The new video-game system Dan had sent Richard Robert was proving to be something of a challenge between man and machine. There was no doubt in her mind about the eventual winner, but the question was, when?

On her belly, stretched full-length along the couch, Shelly languidly watched the set-up-plug-in process. She could have taken a nap, but Dan was having too much fun for her to fall asleep and miss it.

With another muffled oath, Dan stuck his head up from behind the console TV, grinning recklessly. "Almost got it this time," he bragged, and disappeared again with his screwdriver, dozens of black cables and a mangled instruction booklet.

"Hmm." Smiling to herself, Shelly reached down to touch Richard Robert's dark hair. Her brother was having a great time with his new gift. Arms locked around the empty game box, he had fallen asleep on the thick, pile rug in front of the sofa nearly ten minutes ago.

"I remember my father used to swear when he put things together. With the same inflection and gusto as you're using," she commented lazily after a mild string of epithets issued again from behind the television. "Must be a man thing...one of those unique male rituals they teach little boys in the tool aisle at the department store."

She paused, reaching around her brother to pick up and read the back blurb on the game cartridge that had been included with the system. Complicated, she thought, a little, but Richard Robert could do it. In fact, it looked to be a great game. Daniel James Sutherland was a very nice man to have thought of it. A sly grin narrowed her eyes and tugged at her mouth. There had to be a number of ways to thank him. The possibilities were endless. But that was for later. If he ever came out from behind the television.

"His...my father's," she continued conversationally, "most creative swearing was done when he used power tools. I never did understand his love-hate relationship with the electric drill. Listen, are you sure you don't want me to hold your nuts and bolts?"

"Shelly?"

"Yes, Dan?"

"Don't you have some female-puttering thing to do?"

"Yes, Dan."

Rolling over onto her back, Shelly smothered a jaw-cracking yawn and found herself grinning at the ceiling. She thought about adding another log to the fire, but the blaze burned bright and the room was already warm and cozy.

Dan hadn't kissed her yet, not properly, but every time he smiled, with each look he gave, his eyes made promises. Like an excited child with a golden secret, Shelly hugged the anticipation to herself. She flipped onto her stomach again, settling her chin on her folded arms, and searched her mind for something else to keep her occupied. Her gaze fell to the goodies under the tree.

"Dan? Just give me one hint. If I have to wait much longer, I'll be too old to enjoy what's in those boxes. Come on, tell me what the presents are?"

From behind the television came a chuckled, "Greedy woman," followed immediately by a muffled grunt. "Dammit all, what is *this* thing? Why don't they just say an engineering degree is required to hook this blasted game up. Maybe this will work." Then, after a minute, he said, "Tell me more about your family. When did your father die?"

Slowly, the grin left Shelly's mouth, and for a moment, one split second, the room became a watery blur. "When I was nineteen. Later...after...the doctor told me his body had worn itself out, but officially it was his heart. He was only forty-four years old."

"How did you get along with him?"

Shelly stared at her brother's sleeping form for a long time. Her answer, when it came, was slow and thoughtful and stark. "I think he loved me. He wasn't one to talk about how he felt, how things affected him. He was always so concerned about what would happen when he was gone...with Richard Robert I mean, that there was never time for us...he and I. Because it was so important to provide for Richard, he worked and worked and not much else. Before I was twenty, he grew old and died."

Finished at last, Dan came out from behind the TV, listening intently. During the past few weeks, he'd given this subject too much thought and the opening was too convenient to let it go now. He was silent for a long minute, then murmured, "So, one point of view might hold that because of Richard Robert, your father left you."

Shelly went quiet. All of a sudden the room seemed a bit chilly. Angling her head along the plump sofa cushion, the better to watch him, she said slowly, "That is one way of looking at it."

"What about your mother?"

Dan's voice was too bland, the inquiry too offhand, to be taken innocently. Shelly's joyous mood of moments before lost its lustrous shine. "What about her?"

"Nothing much." He shrugged and managed to look busy doing nothing more than rearranging a screwdriver and some cable packaging. "I just remember you said something to the effect that she left the family after Richard Robert was born."

"That's right. I'm sure there were problems between her and my father before then, but they must have come to a head at that time. I've since heard that nothing can bring more strain or guilt to a marriage than the birth of a disabled child."

Dan shook his head. "Lousy timing if you ask me. Other children in the family wouldn't know about adult arguments and conflicts. A very young child would only understand that because of a new brother, a parent left...and then was killed in an automobile accident on the way. Double tragedy. Double trauma."

"Is there a point to all this?" Shelly asked after a long, tense silence.

Dan forced himself to ignore her recoil from his deliberate words and to continue, even though what he said would wound her. "Only that it seems like the pattern of your life is forever repeating itself. Everyone leaves Shelly Barker. First her mother, then her father. And let's not forget the shining moment when Mr. Wonderful made his exit, ostensibly because of Richard Robert."

Shelly wanted to move, but she was trapped by words that until now had lived only in a small, dark corner of her mind. She was confused—hurt...angry...*hurt*. What was he doing? Everyone was entitled to secrets.

"How many other people have come and gone in your life, darlin'? Possible friends...possible lovers? People who didn't understand about dragons and trolls. People you chased away because of them."

Shelly kept very still. She'd discovered that if she moved, even blinked, his words stung more, like little bits of sharp stone and grit flaying all her tender, private places.

"Why are you saying these things?" she whispered. "You're spoiling everything. Why?"

"Because of Richard Robert, everyone you've ever loved has left you. Would you say that about sums up the belief system around here, Shelly?"

Abruptly, shoulders rigid, head bowed, she turned away from him. "I love my brother. Never has it been his fault."

She would have left the sofa, the room itself, but Dan was quicker. Without disturbing the sleeping man on the floor, he managed to trap her slight body between his much bigger one and the cushions. Her flinch, when he brought his hands up to touch her, caught him unaware. Pain kicked sharply in his chest, but he had started this thing, and now he had to finish.

Gently stroking, Dan moved his hands from her shoulders to her face. With his thumb, he applied the lightest of pressure under her chin to bring her gaze up to meet his own.

"My point," he said, searching past the hurt and rejection he saw in her eyes, "is that there is no point. What happened to the people around you...happened. Each incident unto itself, no pattern. Not Richard Robert's fault. Not your responsibility. Not everyone is going to leave you, Shelly."

She shook her head instinctively. He finished speaking in a quick, almost rough voice. "I'm not. I'm here and I'm staying...and I can wait until you believe it."

Dan watched her struggle for comprehension, for pride and composure, and if he hadn't ached for her before, he did at that moment. She squared her shoulders, pushed back her hair and scrubbed at her flushed cheeks.

When it finally came, the smile she gave him was almost real. "I believe you believe what you say." Suddenly, she began to laugh. "Did I really say that? There once was intelligence here. Until you showed up, life was at least predictable."

Dan swung up, plucking her from the sofa with him. "But boring, darlin', real boring. When do you suppose Sleeping Beauty will wake up?"

Shelly looked down at her brother. "I don't know. He stayed awake very late last night and was up again early this morning."

"Hurting?" Dan's brows drew together in a quick frown.

"No, excited. Christmas Eve last night, remember? He was determined to see Santa."

"I imagine you stayed up with him."

Shelly glanced away, then back. She took a small bite of her lower lip. "I tried to sleep," she said softly, "but I had to get up... and not to help Richard Robert catch reindeer. I've been having this... dream lately."

"Tell me," he urged softly.

She hesitated, then said, "The first part I can never remember, but I know you and I are there. Then we're in a bedroom, and you're on the bed, nude, waiting for me—lots of billowy drapes, candles and flowers. I come to you and reach out and—" she shrugged sheepishly "—that's when I wake up and find myself doing perverse things with the pillow. I tell you, Dan, it's not natural."

Dan missed a beat. "You honestly have no idea what your little confessions do to me, do you? By the way, did I tell you that I plan on staying here, with you, in your bed... and I want your pillow. Any problems with that?"

"None," she said simply.

"What about Richard Robert? Is he likely to a have problem with the arrangement?"

"We'll have to see. There's never been a man here, at this house, before." Inexplicably embarrassed, she shrugged and turned for the kitchen. "I...when Spencer...I stayed at his place, always."

"Shelly?" Dan's voice stopped her. "Will you give some thought to what I've said?"

Her chin lifted to a stubborn angle. "Which parts? You've said quite a lot."

"Parts *A*, *B* and *C*... all of the above."

"Maybe," she conceded.

"Fair enough," he said, then with a sudden wide grin, he veered toward the Christmas tree. "And since you've been such a good little red-headed girl, it's time."

Shelly looked on as he sank to his haunches and began rearranging the packages under the tree. Of course, she was already familiar with the size-to-weight ratio and rattle-heft factor of every brightly wrapped gift under there. Intrigued, she watched Dan shuffle the packages, then select the heaviest of the big ones.

Her intrigue turned to unease as he lifted the weighty box and carried it into the kitchen. As clues went, he'd just given her a major one and, crossing her fingers behind her back, she followed him in. She hoped her suspicions about the contents of the box were wrong.

He set the gift on the table and stood back with a voilà grin. "You've binge cooked and frozen it all, right?"

Shelly forced a smile. "How did you guess?"

"Now all that needs doing is to heat it up and we can eat... then bed. Is *that* right?"

Dan waved her toward the box and there was nothing else for Shelly to do but to step forward. He was pleased with himself, man smug that he'd done just the right thing. She wanted to kiss his beautiful mouth and cuss. Taking a breath, she went for the ribbon.

As microwaves went, it was a high-tech beauty—turntable, digital touch panel, heat-sensitive dipstick, an inch-thick instruction manual. Everything and more a woman could want. Shelly stroked the metal cabinet with reverent fingers. The push of a button had opened the door, and a light was on inside.

"It's beautiful," she murmured wistfully, swallowing around the growing thickness in her throat.

Another woman might not have appreciated receiving an electronic appliance as the first gift from the man she loved, but Shelly knew there was more of a motive behind this one than convenience. When they'd spoken of these things before, Dan had probably thought she didn't have one because she couldn't afford it.

*Still he did not understand.*

Head down, she sniffed and again touched the the metal cabinet. Turning, she walked to Dan, slid her arms around his waist and held on. "Thank you."

Dan thought she said his name and in the soft sound was all the sadness of the world. He felt helpless. Quite a reaction over a common kitchen appliance. What had he done—or not done?

"I want to know," he growled roughly as he bent his face close to hers and surrounded her with his arms, "how you plan to react over the juicer? I realize I could have been more romantic, but if you bawl, I'll really feel guilty."

"No, I promise." She lifted her head. "A whole kitchen's worth?"

"Right down to the electric mixer and knife-sharpening can opener. I guess I did the wrong thing."

"But for the right reasons." She intended to unwrap every package, to touch and see the pretty things inside. At least she could have that much. But then… "I need to show you something."

## *Chapter Fourteen*

Before she revealed the deep, dark family secrets, Shelly first wanted to have a normal, civilized meal. The last time they'd all sat down together had been a fiasco. She wanted something different this time.

They ate Christmas dinner in the kitchen because her father had never thought to include a formal dining room when he'd built the house. But there were candles in crystal holders on the lace-covered table, linen napkins and polished silver. Those touches were her contribution.

And no matter what else she did throughout the year, Shelly always made an elegant Christmas dress for herself and something for Richard Robert. This year he'd wanted the new department-store suit, but she had gone ahead and made her dress out of the softest, emerald green angora wool. Simply to touch the material had given her a kind of sensory pleasure. So much so that she'd selected a second length, in a bit heavier weight and more masculine color. Instead of making something for Richard Robert from it, she'd made a sweater for Dan.

In the late afternoon of Christmases past, when the meal was just ready and the candles were lit, brother and sister would don their finery and meet to share a toast. "To us," she would sign, lifting her glass, and Richard Robert would echo her.

This year, Dan poured the wine and initiated the toast. Richard Robert accepted the change without question. For a few moments, Shelly resented it. Who was this man to walk into her neat, tidy life and take over? He wasn't supposed to sign anything different, alter years of tradition.

"Thank God for food."

What kind of a Christmas toast was that? So it was an admirable attempt for someone with limited signing skills, so what? For ten full seconds she resented his intelligence and humor, his white teeth and his perfect smile that could charm innocents like Richard Robert and beguile the jaded, like herself.

For years, since her father's death, there had been only two. Shelly was used to it that way. She was used to having dominance over the family nucleus and, as Dan and Richard Robert interacted, she realized how much life would change if Dan did stick around. She would have to move over and relinquish some of the control she had in her brother's life—and her own.

"You're frowning. Was my toast that bad?"

"No, not too bad," she muttered, adjusting the cowl collar of her dress. "I guess I was thinking of something else. What did you say?"

"That's just it," he said with a self-mocking half smile and a shrug. "I don't know what I'm saying... or rather, what Richard Robert is asking? I'm only up to the alphabet and not very fast at that. Would you interpret until I get the hang of this a little better?"

Shelly's rebellion quickly faded. The Barkers were not the only ones whose lives would have to change. Turning to her brother, she put her wineglass aside and gestured slowly, speaking the words aloud so that Dan could see the signs she used.

"Talk slowly," she told Richard Robert and, after a moment of listening, began to interpret his questions... in a bright, brittle rush. "He wants to know if you're going to be our husband and put a baby seed in my belly... and he wants to know if you'll play the video game with him, and he forgot your name. You'll need a name sign."

"What?" Dan shook his head in amazement. "My what?"

"It's easier to have one," Shelly explained. She brushed her right thumb down across her cheek in the sign for *girl,* then brought her two index fingers together for *same.* Still using her right hand, she tapped an *S* fist lightly on her left shoulder, *Shelly.*

"Girl-same, Shelly. Sister Shelly. That's who I am to Richard Robert, and that's how they know me at the group home. You can finger spell your name every time, but it's better to have a name sign."

"What if I use a *D* on the shoulder, like you use *S?*"

"That would work."

Watching closely, Dan shoved his hands into his pockets while Shelly translated. "Also, tell him yes for me, will you? He and I can play video games for a while, later."

"He'll like that," Shelly said, and she shared a quick smile with her brother.

"But Shelly?"

"Hmm?"

"Tell him I can't play very long, not tonight. You and I have some baby-seed planting to do."

The smile left Shelly's mouth. Her hands fell slowly to her sides. "You'd want children?" she asked, mentally finishing the sentence, *with me?* Closing her eyes, she hoped the sudden, pitiful explosion of longing in her heart was not reflected on her face. One of the hardest things she'd ever done was to keep her voice lightly amused now. "Or are you just talking about fun sex?"

Dan spread his hands. "Can't children be made through the process of fun sex?"

Shelly reached for the back of her chair and, pulling it away from the table, sat down. It was time, she decided, to get the meal started. Dan didn't know that of all the tender places he'd probed today, this one was immeasurably sensitive, the easiest to bleed. Children were a subject she rarely let herself dwell on, let alone joke about.

"I believe," Dan said to Richard Robert, who couldn't hear a word, "your girl same is telling us to sit down, be quiet and eat."

Shelly flashed him a neutral glance. She shook out her napkin and picked up her fork, pointing the tines at him as she said coolly, "Of course, you may speak."

Quizzically, Dan tipped his head. "Was it something I said? What about children, Shelly? Don't *you* want them?"

What was he trying to do? she wondered. Make her suffer? She swallowed and forced herself to meet his gaze. "My mother's great-uncle was deaf," she explained quietly, "so although Richard Robert's mental retardation is a result of massive birth trauma, his deafness might be hereditary. The doctors were never able to substantiate the theory...and my mother had no family left to get a full medical history from, but that's what they think. I could be a carrier of the disability."

"So like everything else in life," Dan pointed out thoughtfully, "it would be a risk."

Shelly looked at him for a long minute. Then she asked one soft, dead-aim question. "Is it a risk you'd be willing to take with a child of your own, Dan?"

Before he could answer, she got up from the table and went to rattle things around in the refrigerator. Surely she remembered seeing a bottle of green olives somewhere. There was catsup, a jar of ranch dressing, coffee and a carton of eggs older than dirt. She pushed aside two pies, one pumpkin, one cream. The more she moved and shuffled the contents, the more frustrated she became. She was very much afraid that if she didn't find those olives, she would disgrace herself and cry.

She didn't hear Dan leave the table and come up behind her, but she felt his arm as it slipped around her waist, and for a second, the most fleeting of moments, she welcomed the comfort of his shoulder as he gathered her close against his side. His voice when it came was a quiet rumble above her head. "Is that what's bothering you, Shelly? That Mr. Wonderful was too much of a coward to take a gamble with you?"

"It was the main reason he left, yes." And if the ache never completely went away, she'd learned to live with it. She wiped at the tears in her eyes, dashing them away before they could fall. "I told you, he couldn't take the chance of having less than his perfect 2.3."

She strained against Dan's hold. "Don't you dare feel sorry for me. Who would want a jerk like that hanging around their children anyway?"

Dan growled and gave her a small shake. "Amen," he said and repeated it. "Don't *you* dare get teary eyed when you think of that jerk, ever again." Like a match to tinder, the sight of those tears for another man had ignited his temper to a flashpoint anger. "He's the past. *I'm* your future. If I say we're going to talk about having kids, then we'll talk. Have you got that, Shelly Barker?"

She lifted her face, thrusting her chin up to meet the challenge. "What? You get all the say?"

He wanted to shake her again, a good one this time. But he had to smile, too. He liked the idea of being kept on his toes by this bullheaded woman, and he *very* much liked the thought of having a miniature one call him Daddy. At that moment, Dan could think of nothing that promised more richness. Life with a couple of mean, orange-headed females would never be boring.

He bent his head and shoved his own nose right back at her. "I do," he said, "and it's about time you realized it. Now, do we fight...eat...or plant baby seeds?"

He was close, too close, for Shelly to be able to keep the heat in her anger. A false anger anyway, and he knew it, covering up her insecurities and foibles. It wasn't even a good act, but it made her feel less vulnerable...less exposed.

"I've said it before and I'll say it again, you are a damned pushy man."

"Yeah? What are you going to do about it?"

"First I'm going to sit down and enjoy the Christmas dinner it took two days to prepare." A quick, flickering glance toward the table showed that Richard Robert had begun to help himself to the feast. She knew then that they had better hurry, and she went back to the table without the olives.

Before sitting, she took one instant longer to look at Dan. "After we've eaten," she said quietly, "I may be willing to negotiate your other two options. Oh, no...everything is cold!"

"That's easy." Reaching around, Dan picked up a platter of carved turkey. "We'll reheat in the microwave."

"Of course," she murmured, and hoped she didn't look as feeble as the drag of her smile felt on her face. She'd forgotten for a moment. They did still have that bit of business to take care of.

She put it off as long as she could. Excuses were handy things, and Shelly wasn't above using all she owned. Dinner had to be eaten leisurely, because, after all, it was Christmas. She couldn't leave the kitchen a mess, and there were gifts to open and admire.

Dan seemed genuinely taken with Shelly's gift to him—a porcelain figurine of a knicker-clad, brown-eyed boy pulling the flyaway pigtail of a little red-headed girl. He said he liked his sweater; he even put it on. She exclaimed over every one of the time-saving appliances, and she was, in fact, awed with the concept of a push-button-controlled blender-hand mixer. There were also two more video games to play.

Finally when all the new gadgets had been stacked neatly on the kitchen table and Richard Robert sat in front of the TV, entertained by the last of the season's animated specials, Shelly led Dan to the top of the basement steps.

The light switch was on the wall and as she reached for it, she hesitated, eyes flashing an unconscious apology to the man behind her.

One bare light bulb illuminated the top of the steep, narrow steps and another swung from a cord at the bottom. The empty, wood-skeleton frames of half-finished rooms smelled of heater, dank cement and laundry detergent. Shelly led the way to the door of the only finished room in the basement. With a hushed, quiet expression on her face, she found the light and stepped aside to let Dan through.

His stunned gaze landed to the left and slowly began traveling to the right. Slow cookers, three of them in dusty, illustrated cartons, sat stacked atop each other on a low shelf and higher, he counted two Seal-A-Meal units and a Fry-Daddy deep fryer. A pink ice-cream maker vied for space with a toaster oven and next to that, a Hurry Hot Grill Center separated two identical fourteen-speed blender boxes. There was more, much more, filling other spaces, stacked on makeshift tables.

"What is all this?" Dan asked in a soft, awed voice.

"The boneyard," Shelly said just as quietly. "Gifts... years of thoughtful gestures from friends, tokens from clients, suppliers...whoever."

She waited until Dan had taken a second, more thorough survey before she continued. "Do you know—" she waved a vague hand toward one of the shelves "—that if you put the wrong cookware or aluminium foil in a microwave, you can short out the wiring system of an entire house? Have you any idea how many common household products can start a fire in a toaster?"

"Richard Robert?"

"I've mentioned—haven't I mentioned?—he's curious about everything. He tried to waffle his hand once. Luckily he didn't hurt himself too badly that time. In case you didn't notice upstairs just now, I have to lock away the remote-control unit for the TV unless I'm with him. To date, he's disassembled four of them. I'll have to monitor his new game system, but I don't mind about that. He...experiments."

Dan took a second longer to look around. Even with the light on, there were shadows in the cramped room. It was dark in the corners, and musty. "I take it he doesn't like to come down here?"

"No, he...no. He doesn't like the basement." Shelly shrugged. "For a while, I kept some of these things upstairs, locked away in a cabinet. I'd go ahead and use them, then put them back." She crossed her arms around her middle and hugged. "In the last few years it's become something of a compulsion with him. Richy always knew those things were there, but he suddenly began to destroy the locks . . . one time, the cabinet itself, to get to them. I can't explain."

Dan shook his head and, rocking forward on the balls of his feet, he shoved his hands deep into his trouser pockets. "Was this before or after Mr. Wonderful?"

She let out a short, confused breath. "After. Why?"

An indecipherable expression crossed his face. Then he smiled a little and stood aside to signal that he was ready to leave. "Did you ever consider Richard Robert might have chosen that way to express his anger?" He made the suggestion to her back as they walked up the steps. "Pay-back for the time you left him. After all, you did something he didn't like. He might be feeling within his rights to do the same . . . destroying property, making your life miserable."

Shelly had already explored that theory on her own. And while it was the most plausible of the reasons she'd managed to come up with, the problem itself remained. That one and a few more like it.

Dan Sutherland might have been a stronger man than the other one had ever pretended to be, but sooner or later he was bound to resent the many limitations that would be placed upon his life by the Barkers.

"Shelly?"

"Hmm?" She blinked, as she came from shadow into the full light of the hallway, then looked around at him.

With his toe, Dan pushed the basement door closed while, with impatient hands, he reached for her. "I appreciate the tour," he said, "and I'll think about what you've told me, but right now . . . would you say—" he brought her back against his chest "—we've been arguing?"

Shelly's body went boneless. He took her full weight and pushed her hair aside to reveal a small ear, the side of a fragile, but stubborn jaw, a slender white throat with its quick, giveaway pulse. With a thumb under her chin, he angled her head, giving himself free access to anything he chose to nibble.

"Argue?" she echoed in a husky, distracted voice. "Have we been?"

"I don't think so." Dan felt his own blood quickening. He'd been good, damned good, all day. Sensitive to her moods, careful of all her odd little fears and quirks. "So, do you wanna take the first punch, or should I?"

Now it was his turn. He'd let her put him off, delay and hedge, but now he was through. Her dress was a pretty thing, draped and molded to the slight, elegant contours of her body. And soft, nearly as soft as the warm, scented flesh it covered. He wanted it gone.

The instant Dan touched her, Shelly's mind began to cloud over. She had been thinking about this moment for so long, wanting it so much that the reality went through her in a giant shudder. With his arm locked around her middle, holding her to the strength of his big body, and the proof of his desire growing boldly against her back, Shelly had the greatest difficulty understanding mere words. "First punch? What does that mean?"

"We're going in order, remember? Food...fight... and—"

"Dan!" Shelly jerked and turned in his arms to face him, head thrown back with faint shock.

"Frenzy, darling. Food...fight...and frenzy. Yours and mine." He smiled into her eyes, a long slow smile. "We've done the food. Now if we get the fighting over with, we can get on to the good part. That's what I meant. Do you want to take the first swing, or should I?"

Shelly put a hand up to his cheek, not with pain in mind, but to urge him closer. If he would bend, she could stretch. His arousal was insistently bold against her belly. She thought that if she could just have a taste of his mouth, she would never need anything else.

With a sudden, reckless little laugh, she caught him off guard, pushing, trapping him against the basement door. The landing was shielded from the kitchen by a half wall. There was no one to see what she did to him, no one to hear him call out. Her pale blue eyes went from his watchful, waiting ones to the distinct, half smiling curve of his mouth. She touched the tip of her tongue to her own bottom lip.

"Give it to me," she finally said, "or I will have to hurt you."

"I don't know," Dan said slowly. There was humor in his voice, but a faint somberness behind his smile. "You can't just use me." He moved his head so that there would be no mistake when she looked at him. "I am staying, Shelly. I want you to tell me you believe that much."

A shadow fell across her face, darkened her eyes. "Dan, please, don't spoil it. I—"

"No, no excuses, no evasions. Tell me. I need to hear that much from you."

He was right. The time for evasion was long past. But she couldn't lie to him, either; would not, even *for* him. So she put a small hand on either side of his face, kissed each corner of his mouth and gave him what she could.

"I, Shelly Barker, love you, Dan Sutherland. And I know that right now, at this minute, you believe you love me."

Dan closed his eyes on a long, disappointed sigh, but when he opened them again, a hint of laughter was back. "You are a stubborn woman, Shelly Barker. You love me, hmm?"

"You already know it," she accused, her eyes narrowing, "so don't let it go to your head."

He rolled the head in question to ease the tight knot of tension in his back and neck. This was proving much more difficult than he'd thought it would be. When he finally worked up the last bit of nerve needed, he spoke quickly. "But you love me, you said so... and, yes, I did have some suspicions. That's why I... ah, hell!"

His hand slid deep into his pants pocket, as it had had a habit of doing lately. This time, instead of jingling change, he pulled out his key ring. It was awkward, but he managed to keep an arm hooked around her waist, anchoring her to him in case she decided to bolt, while at the same time searching through the half dozen keys. Eventually he found what he wanted and worked the object loose. Getting it from his hand to Shelly's proved no problem at all. She was, he decided, probably in some kind of shock.

"A ring." Shelly stated the obvious as she held up her hand. "A diamond ring." Intelligence left her.

"What did you think," Dan teased softly, "that I was going to stop with a blender? What kind of a Santa Claus would I be? Merry Christmas, darlin'."

The mind was a terrible thing to lose. Glancing at Dan, Shelly saw the smug smile on his mouth stretch to a grin. She felt slow and sluggish and stupid. "A diamond engagement ring... on my finger... from you."

"You may get maudlin now," he offered magnanimously, seeing she was coming out of her trance, but he held himself ready in case she decided to take a swing. "Kiss me all over in humble gratitude if you want, my face, my body... my body. You may—" he bent his head, pointing to his cheek "—begin here. I'll accept adulati—" He straightened to his full height with a quick jerk and looked beyond her. "Slow down, partner. You'll have to go slower if you want me to understand."

For a moment longer, Shelly's attention remained riveted on the emerald-cut diamond flashing brilliantly from the third finger of her left hand. It was a beautiful ring, perhaps the most beautiful she had ever seen. Slowly she raised eyes from it. "You can't do this," she said in a scared little voice, and then followed Dan's gaze with her own. "What do you want, Richard Robert?"

Her brother didn't step near the basement door; he refused to get that close. Shelly watched him and when he was done, she shook her head. "Not now," she signed in answer. "Later."

"I can do anything I damned well please," Dan growled back, before turning his attention to Richard Robert. He had got perhaps one sign out of ten, recognizing only the gesture for eat. "Don't tell me he's hungry again?"

"Okay, I won't tell you, but he wants a snack." Again she signed to her brother, "Not now, later."

"How?" she asked Dan. "This isn't the Middle Ages. You can't force me to accept this ring... to marry you."

"I didn't bring it with the intent of forcing you to do anything... Richard Robert, your sister said, *'Not now.'* Wait for us in the kitchen. We will get to you."

Shelly fell back against the wall. She'd seen it once before, but only the tip of the iceberg. Angry, Dan Sutherland was, indeed, an awe-inspiring man. She swallowed, but could find no trace of bravery in herself; her backbone was gone and the only defense she could summon was a pitiful little parry of bravado.

"It doesn't do a bit of good to yell at a deaf man. He can't hear any of what you say."

Dan slowly turned his head and looked down his straight, perfect nose at her. "Then why," he questioned in a carefully controlled voice, "is he back in the kitchen, exactly where I asked him to go?"

"Because you frightened him with your angry face. You scare me too—Lord, you do." She bit her lip and looked away.

"Dan!" Shelly suddenly blurted out. "Did you tell your mother? I mean, does she have any idea you're proposing to the dressmaker? And what about babies? What if we had a less-than-perfect one? All right, so sex is great and we think we love each other—now. That's the easy part. What if—"

"*You* can hear me," he said. Grasping her head between his hands, he tilted her face up firmly. "So listen to this..." Just before he brought his mouth down he told her, *"Be quiet."*

His kiss was hard, not brutal, but angrily impatient. Her start of surprise jolted through him, and he felt her resistance. He ignored both, hauling her closer, pressing harder, wanting more. Her lips parted, probably to protest the treatment. Again, he didn't care. He thrust his tongue past her small teeth and took what he wanted. He was a man of the nineties, but this was his woman, and she was giving him grief. To hell with being a nice guy.

She had such a small, slender body, a dancer's suppleness. One of his large hands left her face to glide over her shoulder and down her back, contracting at her narrow waist. If she felt good in that oh-so-soft dress, he knew she was even softer, more delicate without it.

Then without Dan knowing exactly how it happened, the flavor of the kiss began to change. It didn't belong exclusively to him anymore, but to both of them. With the slightest, subtle shift of her body adjusting to his harder, unyielding one, Shelly forced him to share. The shy entrance of her tongue into his mouth made him regret his selfishness, and when he brought his other hand to rest along the base of her throat, feeling the light, frantic pulse there, his anger gave way to a slow, deliberate gentleness. If he could make her helpless, make her cling and shiver against him, acceptance of the ring would come.

"You make me crazy," he growled against her mouth. At that moment it was the closest he could come to an apology. "Never argue with me again."

Head back, Shelly looked at him with dreamy, passion-heavy eyes. "No, never."

"Liar." He nipped at her bottom lip. "Okay, so we've got through the food and now the fight. Let's get your brother taken care of and get on with the frenzy."

"Yes," Shelly said, but she didn't move. She couldn't.

The more quickly Richard Robert was settled, the more quickly she and Dan could get on to more . . . pressing business. Laughing softly, Dan propped her against the wall and stepped out into the kitchen.

No more than a heartbeat of time could have passed before she heard, "Shelly?"

And her name, said in just such a way, had her hot blood taking a rapid cool. She knew that neutral tone of voice with its what-now inflection. Of course, she knew it. Richard Robert was up to some kind of trick and Dan hadn't the signing skills or the knowledge yet to guess what those tricks could possibly be.

Dan was close. On shaky legs, she moved around the half wall into the kitchen and saw just how close. Not more than a step away. She followed his gaze across the room . . . and the instinctive laughter that rose like a bubble in her throat when she first saw her brother turned to an audible gasp of dismay.

Richard Robert had obviously tired of waiting for them and decided to take matters into his own hands. To one side, just in view on the counter, was a plastic mixing bowl and an upended half-pint container of cream. The kind needing to be whipped in order to make it light, fluffy and edible on pumpkin pie.

He'd got that right and had chosen the right kitchen appliance from among all the new ones stacked on the table; the stainless-steel push-button-controlled hand mixer with bread making capabilities and automatic beater-eject feature.

It wasn't the fact that Richy *had* the mixer out that caused Shelly's heart to suddenly kick in her chest. It was *how* he held it—feet spread, arms locked straight in front and together, hands steady, holding the mixer with spinning beaters directed toward Dan. In his mind he was holding a weapon, like all the cops on every TV show in prime time had ever held theirs on the bad guy.

"I believe," Dan murmured softly, "he's angry enough to shoot...or jealous enough to."

"Don't joke."

"Hell, darlin', I'm not. Even if he can't shoot, he just might try throwing it, beaters and all. Being related to you, he's bound to have a damned good arm."

The little breath she drew was a quick, half gasp. There just might be firing capabilities if Richard Robert hit the auto eject button right. Shelly frantically signed for him to turn it off and put the thing down. He refused with a stubborn shake of his head, and since his hands were full, he escalated the decibel level of his ba-hum. Always a bad sign.

A terrible sign, actually. The portent of impending disaster, of looming doom.

With the sixth sense of one who realized how swiftly and unexpectedly disaster can strike, Shelly knew exactly the moment Richard Robert's finger went for the beater-eject button. It was the same moment he switched his attention from her to Dan and steadied his aim. She knew they were in real trouble when she saw Richy stumble back with the recoil. Incredibly, the missile was launched.

## *Chapter Fifteen*

Frigid night wind blew through, shrieking out from the mouths of Big and Little Cottonwood canyons. Giant ice blasts of breath wailing with fury, haplessly toppling metal cans laden heavily with Christmas day debris, rattling windows like chains and freezing snow-slushed roads into treacherous iced ones on its rampage to the valley below.

The storm reflected the mood of the man. Dan felt no less outraged.

With the blackened tip of the metal poker, he absently jabbed at the glowing embers under the new log he'd just added to fire. From time to time his hand clenched and unclenched into a convulsive fist of remembered ferocity. Never in his life had he thought of hitting someone smaller or weaker than himself—a woman, a child—never.

Until tonight.

Dan had learned a great deal about himself in the span of a few minutes. One, he wasn't as civilized as he'd always thought himself to be. Two, under the right circumstances, anyone was capable of losing control. Three, he had a damned powerful set of lungs. A few useless home truths. As had already been pointed out, roaring at a deaf person made no sense.

Dan could turn a bewildered face to the heavens and protest, "I'm not a violent man!," but the fact was, he'd lifted Richard Robert Barker by the scruff of the neck, shaken him like a dusty rag and had been fully prepared to knock him through the most convenient wall.

Dan acknowledged what he'd done, but he was having a hard time accepting that he was capable of such a blind rage. For a moment, he had lost complete control. He'd snapped.

His first thought upon stepping around the kitchen half wall was that the situation was too bizarre. His impulse had been to laugh. Then he'd called to Shelly.

Shelly had been the first to realize what Richard Robert was going to do. She'd been one pulse beat ahead of Dan. There had been no time for her to think. He'd seen her blank surprise a split second before she reacted, knocking him back a stumbling step with a flying, ninety-seven-pound tackle, shielding his body with her own.

Perhaps if she hadn't been clinging so tightly to protect him, he would not have felt the impact of those metal beaters as they had slammed into her narrow back. Dan swore he'd felt it himself... a piercing, sharp rocket of pain shuddering all the way through her to him.

Perhaps if she hadn't given that one, terrible little moan or slumped in his arms, just for those few seconds, he might have had a chance to stay rational. But she had, and he had not.

He now knew what it was to be caught in a mindless fury. He remembered hearing someone shout, no, not shout, roar. And he also remembered a faint incredulity when he'd realized the noise was his own. But from there his mind was a blur of red haze. He must have crossed the room, somehow taking Shelly with him. How else could she have been there so quickly, throwing herself between his fist and the thrashing of her disabled brother? How else—

The burning log of lodgepole pine chose that moment to sizzle and crack, showering sparks with each rapid-fire snap.

When Shelly came out from tending to Richard Robert in his room, *if* she came back out, Dan would speak to her. He wasn't about to apologize for what he'd done...*almost* done, but he wasn't proud of it, either.

Shelly stood in the shadow of the hall just outside the living room entrance, watching as Dan poked and prodded the fire. Ever since it had happened, he had been so aloof, so coldly unapproachable, that she hesitated to go forward. All during the evening she'd searched her mind for words to say, but so far, nothing had occurred to her.

Dan sensed her presence before he actually saw her. "You can come in, Shelly. I'm not going to bite you."

She hesitated a moment longer, then entered the room with a determined smile. "I didn't think you were."

"Oh?" His frown pulled a tight furrow across his forehead, and his pause lengthened. "Then why are you standing fifteen feet away from me, wringing your hands?"

"I'm—" She started to make a denial, then looked down at herself and realized she was, indeed, standing in the middle of the room, making odd little rubbing motions with her hands. "I'm only ten feet away, not fifteen." She instantly put her hands behind her back.

Dan watched her nervous, stiff steps as she went to sit on the couch. The pillow she immediately grabbed, plumped and picked at remained on her lap, held in front of her like a shield. Bracing a foot on the hearth, he watched her for another long moment, noting that she still wore the ring. At this point, however, that fact didn't tell him much.

"How is he?" Dan asked finally, referring to Richard Robert and the younger man's near hysteria when they'd last been together.

"He stopped crying quite a while ago. When I left he was much calmer, almost asleep. You frightened the hell out of him." Shelly worked up the courage to continue. "But, Dan, you didn't hurt him."

"I wanted to." Dan's voice tightened, "When those things hit you...I honest-to-God wanted to."

"I know," she said, then ducked her head to pick at a loose thread in the pillow. "I saw it in your face. Richard Robert saw it."

"And did I scare you, too, darlin'?"

"Yes, you did." She tried to smile.

"I didn't mean...I... Hell!" In disgust, he shook his head and changed the subject. "How are you feeling? Will you let me see the damage? It was your shoulder, wasn't it?"

"It's not so bad. I'm sure the skin isn't broken." Her eyes widened as Dan left the fireplace and approached the couch. All the saliva in her mouth seemed to dry up, and she swallowed hard as he sat down next to her. "There should—" she cleared her throat "—only be a bruise."

"Only a bruise," he echoed softly, finding under her hair the zipper at the back of her dress, "that should have been mine." Sliding the tab down a fraction of an inch, he pressed his lips to the side of her neck. "If those had been bullets, you would have saved my life, Shelly Barker."

Bit by bit, the tension that had been holding Shelly in a rigid, upright position lessened, and she found herself leaning against him as Dan carefully eased the dress away from one shoulder. He seemed determined to get the thing off, and the idea did have merit.

"Dan?"

"Uh-hmm?"

"Could you kiss me better again? Not on my neck this time, but on my mouth. My mouth hurts." Big eyed, she nodded solemnly when he angled his head to look at her. "I swear, it really does."

"I will," he promised tenderly. He thought he might be able to smile again; not now, but sometime soon. "I want to see the bruising first."

"And Dan?"

"Hmm?"

Turning into his chest, Shelly buried her face against him while her dress was slowly peeled down the other shoulder. "You won't tell anyone, will you?"

"What, darlin'?"

Tears clogged her throat even while laughter trembled through the thickness. She swallowed. "Don't tell anyone that I was—" her voice dropped to a faint, mournful wail "—defeated by a pair of flying . . . egg beaters!"

A sharp, quick breath hissed between Dan's teeth. He might have made more of an effort to share her mood, except for the discovery of a large red area just under her shoulder blade. Already there was purple discoloration; by morning she would have one hell of a black-and-blue contusion. In the end, he could not find anything about this situation amusing.

Sliding his hand beneath her hair, he stroked the side of her neck and jaw. "Has anything like this ever happened before?" he asked with a quiet voice that didn't come easy.

As an experiment, Shelly let herself accept Dan's cosseting. She knew her senses were being strummed by a master hand, but this time she placed no limits on her own enjoyment of it. When his touch became unbearably gentle, she allowed herself the electric shivers. When her mind cautioned moderation, she pushed the warning away. She welcomed the calming lull of his heartbeat under her cheek and the soft stir of his breath in her hair as he bent his head closer. And even when she knew the tack his question was taking, she decided to leave her defenses down and go with him.

"There have been situations in the past that—" she searched for words to answer fairly and accurately "—that have escalated so quickly as to end out of control . . . usually when Richy feels threatened or angry, or when he wants something, or . . ." She gave a faint shrug and shook her head. "This time he was mad, because we told him to wait, and also a little jealous. He didn't like the idea of you kissing me. When I talked to him, he told me he was sorry. He said his heart hurt because I got hurt, but that he had wanted to make you go away."

"He's used to having you to himself."

"Yes," Shelly agreed, "he is. The thing is . . ." She dared say it. "To continue our relationship, it's going to take some adjustment on your part and time on his."

"No, darlin'," Dan said softly, slowly, "I have no intention of adjusting...not if that means giving in to your brother's every mood and whim. No matter what the reason or circumstance. You were hurt tonight. I will not adjust to that. I cannot live my life under those rules."

Shelly looked at the glittering emerald-cut diamond ring on her finger. So, she thought dully, again it comes to a choice. She drew a breath, a long, deep one, and when she felt she could keep her voice steady, she tilted her face and stared straight into his eyes. "Is this an ultimatum, Dan?"

A direct blow. Blood roared in Dan's head. Anger was first, then outraged justice...how dare she question him? Compare him, again! Very slowly he held out a hand and watched it tremble. His face hardened. After all that had gone before, *and* given the fact she was at this moment resting against his body, accepting all the care and tenderness he was capable of giving, how could she even think such a thing?

His voice was grim when he said, "Look, you want your brother to have as much freedom as possible? Well, I've got news for you...nothing is free. If you give Richard Robert the consideration of an adult, you have a right to expect mature behavior back from him. We function within certain bounds, Shelly. Everyone of us is subject to limits."

He took her by the shoulders and gave her a little shake. "Throwing temper tantrums and hurting people when things don't go his way is not acceptable. Remember those trolls and dragons you warned me about? Well, darlin', you set most of them loose yourself. You've got to set some stricter guidelines for your brother. That's the choice you have to make."

"Stricter limits? Boundaries? Those are things you set for children. Richard Robert is a grown man."

"My point then, Shelly, is to expect him to act like one. What if our child had been in that kitchen? What if the next time your brother lost his temper, it was over something the baby did?"

Shelly pulled away from his hands and, clutching the edges of her new Christmas dress up around her throat, looked around almost wildly. "A child! You keep talking about it, but what if we don't have one? What if we do and she's like her uncle?"

"Then she is, dammit!" Dan exploded to his feet and stalked the four corners of the room, turning at the fireplace. "And we set the same boundaries and have the same expectations as we would have for her brother...or sister...with any child."

"You expect too much!" She threw up her hands.

Through the bite of his own anger, Dan saw the weight of despair bowing Shelly's slender shoulders and, despite his conviction, the grim line of his mouth softened. "No," he said quietly, "you *give* too much and expect too little."

Shelly pulled her knees up under the soft material of her green angora dress and wrapped her arms around them. She was beginning to feel the effects of a long day and, dammit, her shoulder hurt.

"I hate to fight over him," she said. Her eyes grew misty even though her whisper was toneless. "All I've ever wanted to do was just...love someone." She stole a glance at Dan across the room. "You. This morning, I waited and waited for you to come." Her gaze shifted back to the fire. "I wanted to love you...and now we're fighting. What happens next?"

Despite his frustration, despite his fear that she would never see what he was trying to show her, Dan knew what he wanted to happen between himself and Shelly Barker. It was the reason he'd come and the reason he would always return.

Carefully positioning the fireplace screen over the opening for the night, he went to her, scooping her up like a child. "First, we make up, and then we make love." He looked at her mouth. "Does it still hurt? Do you want me to kiss it better?"

Dear heavens, she thought on a long, tortuous sigh, she wished it was so. She turned her face into his throat and held on. Though he could kiss her until she shook apart, he could not make her aching heart better.

But he could make her forget, and by some fluke of fate, he wanted her enough to think of giving her a ring. She smiled a little at the thought. Oh, yes, she could make him crazy.

"Umm-hmm," she said, putting her own mouth to the pulse at his neck, feeling his lifeblood rush through his body. "Please, make it better."

Dan caught her up higher, more tightly to him, and began the trip to her room. He made the effort to be especially quiet as they passed Richard Robert's door. "Will he be okay, do you think?"

A smile shaded her voice as she whispered, "Richy is sleeping by now. He'll be fine." She caught the downy soft lobe of his ear between small teeth and gave a delicate tug. "And you don't have to tiptoe—even with army boots on, it wouldn't matter."

At her bedroom, Dan angled his head until their noses bumped. "Then why," he wanted to know, nudging the door open with the toe of his shoe, "are you whispering?"

"Because I," she murmured, nuzzling the exquisitely masculine spot behind his ear, "am breathless."

Excitement darkened her eyes as Dan moved with her to the foot of the bed. She tasted the ridge of his left jawbone with the pointed tip of her tongue, and she was the one who shuddered. Looping both hands behind his neck, Shelly closed her eyes and, when he let go of her legs, began the slow, tactile descent down his body until she stood on her own.

She wanted to tell him a hundred things. Not merely that she missed this, missed him, but how much. There were countless small bits and odd pieces of her life she'd been saving to share with him. She listened to the sound of his breathing in the dark, and while it was comforting, she wanted to see him, to see for herself that he was real and unharmed and as beautiful as when he'd last been in this room with her.

She had been waiting so long, the ache inside was relentless. She lifted a hand. "Can I—"

"For pity's sake . . . touch me, Shelly!"

With the sudden, fearful release of tension, Shelly wrapped her arms around Dan's neck and raising to her toes, pressed her mouth to his chin, his collarbone, anywhere she could reach until he bent his head and she had what she wanted. Using her lips, tongue, and hands she spoke to him, revealing her confusion, telling of nights with no end.

When he pulled her closer, she whimpered and sent her hands down his back to seek warm, bare flesh. For a moment she met resistance, the damned soft sweater she could push aside but not remove and a shirt she had to tug from the waistband of his pants. Her breasts ached to be touched and, sliding her hands under the band of his trousers, she gripped the tight, tensing muscles of his hips and pressed herself up and against him in a wanton invitation.

His groan was thick and guttural. "Do you know how fast I'll explode? Do you know what you're doing?"

She did, and even the threat of eternal damnation could not stop Shelly. There was no laughter in her eyes as she peered up through the darkness at him. A smile was beyond her. The thoughts in her mind had been reduced to the most basic of concepts. Dan was here. He was close enough to make love to.

Wordlessly, she moved her hands to the buckle of his belt and, oh-so-slowly worked it free. For a moment, the sound of the zipper sliding downward drowned out the harshness of his breathing. Shelly's own center was needy, swollen, achey, and she closed her fingers around the relief-giving, undeniable part of him.

"Shelly..." Dan's breath was hard and quick. "Let me get my...ah, darlin', nooo."

She knew what he wanted: time to make it right and words she didn't have. But as strong as he was, he was shuddering under her hands, helpless to stop her. Just as she was helpless to stop. She left the heat of him and pushed at his shoulders so that he fell back upon the bed.

And then there were four hands ripping away at clothes, breaking snaps, popping buttons. Shelly's dress was already open at the back and in one fluid movement Dan had it up over her head and off. Her slip was different, not so easy to remove in his fumbling haste to reach her panties. Between hard, burning kisses, he settled for tearing off her panty hose and pushing the slip above her waist.

Shelly was no less frantic, pushing his sweater, his shirt, tugging on his pants and shorts until she encountered the final barrier of shoes and decided to hell with them. She couldn't wait.

She was bold, more so than she had ever been or thought she could be. Unfastening her mouth from Dan's, she threw a leg over his thighs and positioning herself above him, she filled herself with his power.

Then she set up a rocking motion, and his hands went to her hips to keep her steady because the intensity of feeling would shudder between them and she'd loose the rhythm. She bent and her tongue flicked at his throat, enjoying his flavors, the textures of man, while his hands held her, anchoring her more firmly to him as the rocking quickened and her eyes lost their focus.

"Dan?" Her voice was tiny, scared, like that of a little girl.

She was nearly there. He could see it, feel the instinctive tightening of her body around him. "I'm here," he promised, and he felt his own control slip until he couldn't think.

Need took over, whipping Shelly on, driving her higher. Sensations layered and built until the only thing she could hear was the crash of her own heartbeat and harsh rasp of his breathing. And just when she thought she could take nothing else, Dan gave her more. He took her with him, shuddering, shivering, sobbing, to the edge and over.

Shelly's eyes came open. It didn't seem possible that she was awake again. Her body was exhausted, but her mind would not rest. With a sigh, she sank back against Dan and his arm tightened around her hip. Her movement must have disturbed him, because he snuffled and mumbled a disjointed fragment from his dreams.

She smiled into the darkness and resigned herself to a night spent in bondage. He hadn't let go of her since he'd managed to work his left shoe from the tangled leg of his pants, thrown it across the room and dragged them both to the pillows at the head of the bed. Such an arrogant man. In the nest of his arms, Shelly could not see the illuminated dial of the bedside clock, but she knew it was late.

She had been dreaming, but the why of her little fantasy escaped her. It was the same one that had disturbed her during the three weeks of Dan's absence— A blank piece she could never remember, then Dan nude on the bed, smiling, reaching for her. Why now, she wondered, why again? All she had to do was turn in his arms and the reality of him was more erotic than any dream.

It was warm under the covers and cozy, and…she should have been able to sleep. She closed her eyes and tried counting Dan's heartbeats instead of sheep. Then she started upward from her toes, giving each muscle along the way the command to relax.

It must be, she finally decided, a case of sensory overload. Or she needed the bathroom and a drink of water. Using utmost care not to wake him, she removed Dan's arm and slid from the bed. After locating her slippers beside the bed and her robe on the chair by the closet, she left Dan sleeping.

In the kitchen, the refrigerator bulged with tasties and pastries, but Shelly wanted none of it. She rummaged for a few minutes, thinking she might, but with an unconscious shake of her head, she shut the door and decided to check something else instead.

Richard Robert slept with a plastic, snail-shaped nightlight on, but as Shelly stood just inside his open door, she could only make out a slight form under the mound of quilts. For a moment she thought he might have been the cause of her insomnia, like in some psychic mind-meld link in which she sensed he was in trouble and had to get to him, or that he was up to some Richy trick. But it wasn't that, either. She knew he was well and truly asleep by his deep breathing and irregular sinus snuffles.

On impulse, she went for the key to her workroom. Since she had already made the pattern for the dress, she could start cutting some of the interface pieces. Working on the project would give her something to do until she could decide what she wanted to do or until she could sleep, whichever came first.

Dan woke missing her. The space beside him was cold; the bed was empty. He wondered if there would come a time when Shelly stayed where he put her, then decided probably not. He laughed a little to himself. Throwing back the covers, he swung his bare feet over the edge of the bed and tried to remember where he'd kicked his pants.

He found her by the sliver of light stealing out from under her workroom door. Music was softly playing from an AM station on the radio, but she was so engrossed she did not seem to hear when the song she was humming ended, nor did she notice the announcer screaming details about the upcoming Bad Brains concert, nor did she surface when Dan walked over to turn him off.

Hunched over her worktable, she was perched on a backless stool with one foot tucked under her bottom and the other one swinging free through the wide folds of her robe. He started to say something, then stopped. She had her hair skimmed back over the one pale shoulder left bare by the loose lapel of her oversize covering. The only thing he could see holding the robe together was a belt of the same dark fabric tied and knotted at her narrow waist.

As her leg swung, he caught glimpses of a soft, white thigh, and even as he watched, the motion dislodged the covering from her lap. Any remaining air in Dan's chest was trapped there. He couldn't move or breathe. He was riveted where he stood. Her skin was milk pale, the exposed curls metallic copper.

Preoccupied, Shelly's hand hovered over her lap, over the uncovered nest of bright, silky curls, and then she touched herself, not there, but to run her fingers absently along her hip until she found the edge of the robe and repositioned it across her lap.

Dan had never felt anything like it before. An explosion of urgency. He was a thirty-two-year-old man, yet that one unstudied action was the most sensually breathtaking sight he'd ever witnessed. But more than that. She was simply elegant—clean lines and bones, fire and ice, nerves and laughter. She was not ready to accept the words, so he would show her again and again.

"Shelly." His voice was stark with the control it took to reach, but not fall upon her. "Come back to bed." His voice was gentle because he did not mean to frighten, only to ravish her. "I want to love you again."

Shelly trembled as she stared up into the eyes of her lover. There was something in him, some dark, running emotion she swore had a scent and taste. Arousal, yes, but more than that. Without a word, she put her scissors aside and the sleeves fell back to reveal her white, white arms as she reached for him.

"Yes."

## *Chapter Sixteen*

With her heart full of treasure and her body inert, Shelly knew when she finally fell asleep and began to dream because someone insisted on pinching her toe.

It was not any real someone. Not Daniel James Sutherland. His shoulder was under her cheek and his face was buried in the tangled mass of her hair. She knew she wasn't dreaming that part because his odd little sleep noises dropped right into her left ear. Why, then, would anyone in a sublime REM state dream of foot discomfort?

Unless she was wrong about the dream and right about the discomfort. Prying her good eye open, Shelly used it to glare down the bed. "Richard Robert!"

"Girl-same Shelly wake up." Richard Robert let go of her toe so that he could sign his demands. "Richard Robert hungry. Not like girl-same with man. Bad man. Not make our husband. Girl-same get up. Richard Robert want food now."

When she caught herself automatically reaching for her robe, it occurred to Shelly that Dan may have had a point the night before. It wasn't even six o'clock yet, and she didn't *want* to get up. Infants and invalids were fed on demand, not grown men.

It also occurred to Shelly, as she uncharacteristically hesitated, that while Richard Robert had always been a tad on the demanding side, over the past few years, he'd become downright spoiled.

When was the last time she had even expected him to act civilly toward her... a please, a thank you; never mind respecting her privacy? Not since Spencer. Not since she'd donned the haircloth of misery and guilt.

Tucking the quilt more securely around her chest, Shelly pushed away from Dan. Up on her elbow, she used her thumb and first two fingers, bringing them sharply together in the sign for no. Then she told him, "Richard Robert has to wait. Girl-same Shelly and husband sleep more."

It was like flexing an atrophied muscle. Her resolve had long since gone soft, her expectations flaccid. It was not comfortable to watch her brother pull back in confusion, as if she'd just changed the rules to the only game he knew. Girl-same Shelly *always* did Richard Robert's bidding.

She told him again, "Not eat now. Sleep more, tired. Richard Robert wait. Go out, wait."

And *she* waited, holding her breath to see what came next. Incredibly, after a minute, Richard Robert did as she requested. Not just like that—a bit reluctantly, confusion slowing his steps until he reached the door, a last second-chance glance over his shoulder before he left.

Shelly fell back on the pillow with a whoof, staring straight up at the ceiling with wide, wondering eyes. She brought up a hand to rub the tingling itch on her cheek and discovered, when she turned her head, the itch was from Dan boring holes in her skin with sleep heavy brown eyes.

"What," he asked in a scratchy voice, "was that about?"

Delighted with the world in general and his less-than-perfect morning image in particular, Shelly hitched herself back up to her elbow and stared raptly into Dan's bloodshot, stubbly face. "He wanted breakfast." She dropped a kiss at the corner of Dan's mouth. "You look awful."

"So would you if you'd tangled with a wildcat all night." He yawned and combed his fingers through her hair, stroking it away from her face. Hooking an arm around her neck, he brought her down and closed his eyes to more fully savor her plump, little breasts pushing into his chest. After a drowsy minute, he murmured, "I'll fix him something. I might as well start practicing."

"You won't have to." Her eyelids popped open, for she had been savoring Dan's nearness just as thoroughly and she shared her wonder. "I told him we wanted to sleep a little longer. I asked him to leave the room . . . and wait. And you know what? He did as I asked."

Dan gathered her soft, warm body closer. He let a minute go by, then another one. Then he found her chin, lifted her face up to him, and whispered, "What do you really think he's doing?"

"I don't know," she said in a worried rush, and bit her lip, "but there's a principle at stake now. Some time has to pass."

"Yes," Dan agreed, pulling the covers up higher around them.

"I want Richard Robert to realize that his reign of demand and obey is over."

"It won't be easy."

"No. . . Dan?"

"Hmm?"

"Can you see the clock?"

"I can. Do you think twelve minutes and thirty-seven seconds is time enough to establish the principle of the thing?"

She thought it over. "I think I can live with fifteen." She went quiet. "What if he really is waiting? Just as I asked him to."

"Shelly?"

"Hmm?"

"Thirteen minutes."

"Okay, point proved. I'm up."

The hour of Armageddon—Richy's.

Dumbfounded, Shelly stood in the open doorway of her workroom. Wreckage...not total, but deliberate. Not carnage so much as rebellion. The sketches she had labored over so painstakingly were in tiny butcher-paper pieces all over the hardwood floor. Her bolt of nine-month-wait silk had been unraveled to a yards-long ivory banner draped, looped and tossed around the room. The small bag of pearlescent sequins she'd thought to use and then set aside had been ripped open and tossed.

Nothing that couldn't be fixed. Nothing irretrievably damaged. Hadn't she all but issued this challenge? It could have been worse. Her heavy cutting shears were out in plain sight, along with the lighter ones she'd been using last night. With the many dangerous and valuable things she kept locked up in this room, it could have been disastrous.

But Shelly's world spun and tilted. She found herself on her knees scrambling for the paper tatters of her dress...the dream dress. The blank part of the dream she could never remember was this dress, her in it walking down the aisle toward Dan.

The impractical, impossibly expensive wedding gown she'd already begun to cut the pieces for. Narrow pieces, odd pieces...the one she'd unconsciously made to fit only short, skinny, orange-haired women.

She held the paper litter in her hands and lifted her eyes to Richard Robert huddled across the room, listening to his defensive ba-hum. Not fair, she thought, that he had not even been able to hear her coming. Not fair, but not her fault.

"Shelly?" Only half-dressed, Dan came in to stand, stunned, amid vandalism. "My God, the door...last night. I'm so sorry, darlin'. I'm responsible for this."

"No," she whispered, and shook her head. "Richard Robert is responsible for this. My workroom has always been off-limits." She let the paper shreds fall through her fingers and stood up. "And I'm responsible." She looked at her brother. "But no more. I made a mistake, but the guilt is what's hurting us both the most."

Before she realized what she was going to do, anger exploded in her brain and Shelly was across the floor. Her hands were on Richard Robert's arms and she began to shake him like he was a small boy.

"I...give...you...my...love!" She was too upset to sign and too upset to stop. "I...owe you my...loyalty. But...Richard Robert...Barker—" each word was punctuated with a shake "—I take back my life. That... dress...was...mine, do you understand? My wedding dress! Dan...*will* be...our...husband...he *will*... plant baby seeds...and, by damn, we *will* live happily ever after. *Do...you...hear...me!*"

"Shelly...darlin'!" Dan decided it was time to intercede, not because there was any danger of her doing damage to his future brother-in-law—she hadn't the physical strength for that—but because she was getting all het up and, although there was a ring, there had not been an actual proposal yet.

He took her by the shoulders, pried her loose and turned her around. "Didn't anyone ever tell you it does absolutely no good to yell at a deaf man?"

She glared at him through tear-drenched eyes. "Don't you dare laugh at me."

Drawing her close, he wrapped his arms around her and held on. "Never. I will never laugh at you. Now, tell me, darlin'. Just once, say it."

Shelly tried to speak, but couldn't. She slid her own hands around the smooth, bare skin of his waist and held on right back. "I believe," she said, finally managing to choke out the words, "that while life with the Barkers will never be easy, you'll be here with us...with me."

Dan closed his eyes, feeling love and relief wash through him. His curse, he supposed, was to spend the rest of his life with this stubborn, orange-haired woman. Rubbing his cheek on the top of her head, he smiled. There was one last pound of flesh he intended to collect. "And . . . ? Come on, one time, that's all I'm asking."

Shelly pulled back and blinked until the tears were only glitter in her pale blue eyes. "I love you beyond reason," she whispered. Stretching up on her toes she got as close to his ear as possible to finish gravely, "But you are a damned pushy man."

* * * * *

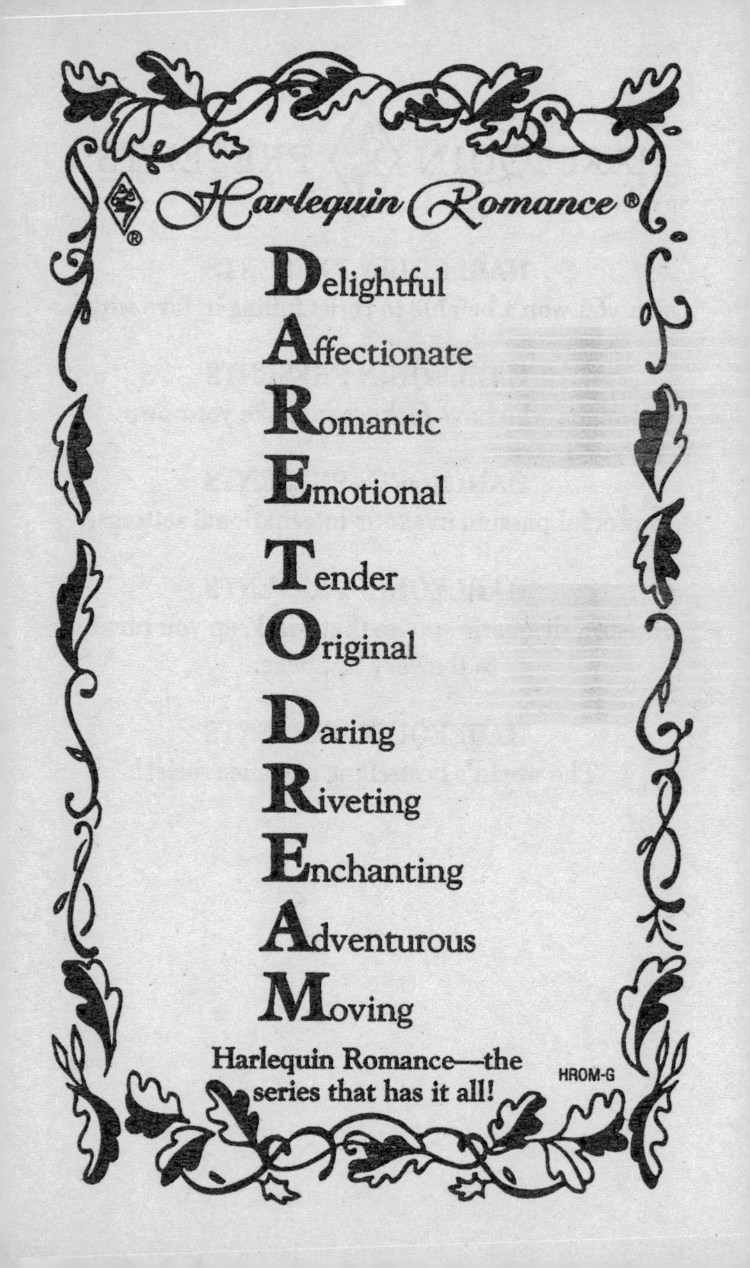
Harlequin Romance®
Delightful
Affectionate
Romantic
Emotional
Tender
Original
Daring
Riveting
Enchanting
Adventurous
Moving
Harlequin Romance—the series that has it all!
HROM-G

HARLEQUIN
PRESENTS®

HARLEQUIN®

INTRIGUE®

# THAT'S INTRIGUE—DYNAMIC ROMANCE AT ITS BEST!

Harlequin Intrigue is now bringing you more—more men and mystery, more desire and danger. If you've been looking for thrilling tales of contemporary passion and sensuous love stories with taut, edge-of-the-seat suspense—then you'll *love* Harlequin Intrigue!

Every month, you'll meet four new heroes who are guaranteed to make your spine tingle and your pulse pound. With them you'll enter into the exciting world of Harlequin Intrigue—where your life is on the line and so is your heart!

**Harlequin Intrigue—we'll leave you breathless!**

INT-GEN

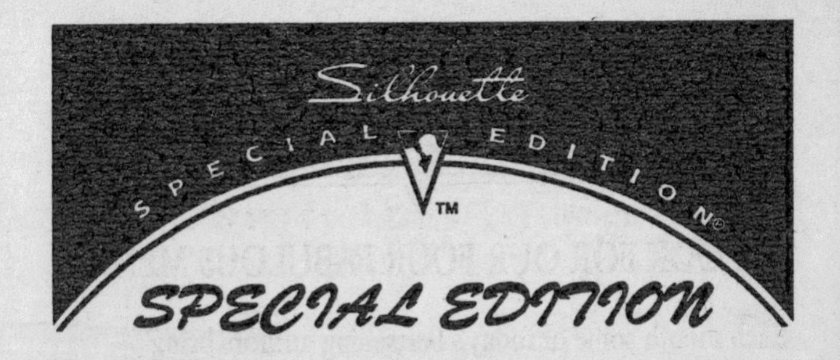
Silhouette
SPECIAL EDITION
TM
SPECIAL EDITION

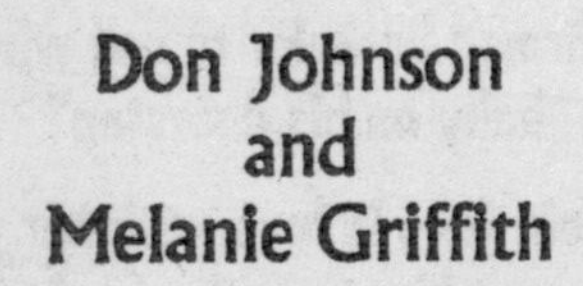

# Don Johnson and Melanie Griffith

Don Johnson and Melanie Griffith began living together when she was only fourteen and he was twenty-two years old. They were together for four years, then married in February 1976. It was his second marriage, and her first. They divorced a year later.

Each went on to other loves—Melanie to actor Steven Bauer, with whom she had a son, Alexander, and Johnson to Patti D'Arbanville, with whom he had a long relationship that also eventually produced a son. But then, Don asked Melanie to appear in an episode of "Miami Vice" that he was directing. The two played such a steamy love scene that NBC insisted on editing it for the rerun. On June 26, 1989, the two were remarried in Colorado. Their daughter, Dakota, was born in October 1989. They have had a much-publicized on-again, off-again marriage, which has now ended in divorce—again.